The
Royal Shakespeare Company's
Centenary Production # HENRY V

The
Royal Shakespeare Company's
Production of

HENRY V

for the Centenary Season at The Royal Shakespeare Theatre

The working text of Shakespeare's play together with articles and notes by the director, designer, composer, actors and other members of the Company, and comments from the critics and the audience.

Edited and with Interviews
by
Sally Beauman

Foreword by
H.R.H. The Duke of Edinburgh

PERGAMON PRESS
OXFORD · NEW YORK · TORONTO
SYDNEY · PARIS · BRAUNSCHWEIG

A. Wheaton & Company
Hennock Road, Exeter EX2 8RP

Pergamon Press Ltd
Headington Hill Hall, Oxford OX3 0BW

Pergamon of Canada Ltd
P.O. Box 9600, Don Mills, Ontario M3C 2T9

Pergamon Press (Australia) Pty. Ltd
19a Boundary Street, Rushcutters Bay, N.S.W. 2011

First edition 1976

Printed in Great Britain by A. Wheaton & Company, Exeter

ISBN 0 08 020874 6

CONTENTS

ACKNOWLEDGEMENTS

A number of people gave me much help in preparing this book. But, in particular, I would like to thank the actors, designer and composer of *Henry V*, who talked to me patiently and at length; Roger Pringle and the Library staff at the Shakespeare Centre, Stratford-upon-Avon; Elizabeth Lane, without whose assistance the book would never have been completed; and Alan Howard and Terry Hands, who – one way and another – had to live with this book for a considerable period of time.

S.B.

The publishers are grateful to Joe Cocks of Stratford-upon-Avon for the cover photographs; to Nobby Clark and Joe Cocks for permission to reproduce photographs of the play; and to Barry Hicks for photographs of Farrah's sets.

This is not an introduction to Shakespeare's Henry V; that would be presumptuous. It is simply to remind you that the Royal Shakespeare Theatre has been going for a hundred years and that it is in great need of help if it is to continue in the future. Unlike the classic masterpieces of literature which can be enjoyed in solitude, the great plays have to be acted out on the stage. Shakespeare must have a theatre and a company of actors to complete his creations. The Royal Shakespeare Theatre has been fulfilling this function with conspicuous success for a hundred years and it is unthinkable that the present and future generations should lose what has become a national institution.

The Theatre made the appropriate choice of Henry V to mark its centenary. The marvellous spirit of the play; the success of the tiny, hungry, ill clad band of troops under its hero-king facing a huge well armed and confident enemy, infects everyone who sees it. I am sure the choice was a good omen and I hope that this book will give heart and courage to the band of supporters of the Theatre to overcome the menace of rising costs and inflation in the years ahead.

THE CENTENARY SEASON

TREVOR NUNN – ARTISTIC DIRECTOR OF THE RSC

The usual form for gloating over centenaries is to contrast the shy, tiny acorn planted a hundred years ago ('Little did they imagine…') with the giant, confident oak ('Who would have believed…') of today. You start with some jokes about early, hair-raising near squeaks. You bring up the organ-music to Meet the Challenge of two World Wars. You end by releasing a triumphal flurry of doves, confetti and recent statistics – biggest, longest, royalest, richest, most.

It didn't feel quite like that in the hundredth year since the incorporation of Charles Edward Flower's Shakespeare Memorial committee in 1875. The statistics were there, all right – the biggest company in the world, playing to the largest audiences, winning the most prizes. The doves and confetti were duly released. But in other respects, the pattern seemed reversed. For the Royal Shakespeare Company, 1975 was a year of hair-raising near squeaks. Both its theatres were in peril. The Royal Shakespeare Theatre in Stratford had to appeal for funds to preserve its very fabric. Its London base at the Aldwych was threatened by inflated costs and insufficient subsidy. For giant, oaken confidence, we could only look back enviously at Stratford's sturdy Victorian mayor and brewer, deciding with his mutton-chopped colleagues that their small Warwickshire market town should be the world's stage and model for playing Shakespeare.

A year, in fact, for stiffening the sinews, conjuring up the blood and imitating the action of a tiger. All of which seemed one more reason for celebrating the centenary by performing a cycle of Shakepeare's *Henry IV, Parts One* and *Two, Henry V* and his other Falstaff play, *The Merry Wives of Windsor*.

The 'Henry' plays have always had a special place at Stratford. It was there, in the early years of the first Memorial Theatre, that Sir Frank Benson and his Bensonians rescued them from more than a century of critical and theatrical neglect. They became the special jewels of his pre-1914 Stratford seasons. Perhaps it was because Henry IV was one of his best roles. Perhaps because, Falstaff apart, they called for little in the way of nineteenth-century 'star acting'. Perhaps because the cricketing young university actors he recruited cast better as Hals and Hotspurs than as Romeos or Hamlets. But mostly, I imagine, it was because the three plays together form a single masterpiece which needs to be seen together, in a festival repertoire, to be appreciated. And because they add up to a national epic, as Coleridge wrote, with a special message of courage to the English in times of gathering darkness, fear and falling empires.

The 'Henry' plays were the centre of Benson's last pre-war season in 1914. They were the opening plays of the new Memorial Theatre in 1932, when it replaced Flower's original Victorian edifice after the disastrous fire of 1926. They were the plays chosen for the Festival of Britain season in 1951–Richard Burton played Hal, Michael Redgrave Hotspur, Anthony Quayle was Falstaff and Harry Andrews Henry IV. And they were the plays selected by Peter Hall to celebrate Shakespeare's quatercentenary in 1964, taking their place in a complete sequence of the history-plays from *Richard II*, by way of the *Henry VI* trilogy, to *Richard III*.

The 1964 season has always seemed to me the point when the RSC first really thought its way to the bottom of the question of how Shakespeare needed to be staged in the 1960s, and came up with an answer and company style shared in common between all its directors and actors. In the decade since then, actors and directors have come and gone, the RSC style has evolved through many mutations and, for me at least, the question of how Shakespeare needed to be staged in the 1970s had raised its head. We all had our own ideas about that, some wildly differing. It seemed time to return to the piece of work which had brought the RSC its original unity, to see what it had to tell us ten years later.

After all, *Henry V* is the nearest Shakespeare came to telling us how he meant his plays to be staged. Its Chorus is explicit about how much stage and actors will do, how much the audience must do for itself.

> *Think when we talk of horses that you see them*
> *Printing their proud hoofs i'th'receiving earth;*

For 'tis your thoughts that now must deck our kings,
Carry them here and there, jumping o'er times,
Turning th' accomplishment of many years
Into an hour glass.

In other words, a theatre of words. Actors on a bare stage conjuring the audience with language and nothing else on to 'the vasty fields of France', the ramparts of Elsinore or Prospero's island. Because the histories demand this more insistently than any other play in the canon, they are the best for bringing a Shakespeare company back to the basic disciplines of such a theatre. Their size and fast-moving variety resist any single, neat directional concept. There is no way a designer can bring on stage literal representations of Shrewsbury field, Shallow's orchard, the breached walls of Harfleur, or the mounted chivalries of Agincourt. In any re-thinking of Shakespearian practice, the histories are an obvious place to start.

Even if time hadn't brought round the need to reconsider our playing of Shakespeare, financial stringency would have forced it on us. Audiences probably worry less than artistic directors about the lack of a single, consistent company style. Ideally, every director would rather create his productions from the ground up, invent his own way of confronting an audience with them, stamp them with his own style, and signature. But our book-keeping told us we could no longer afford this even if we would have preferred it. Unless actors are prepared to starve or return to the benefit system, Shakespeare will always be expensive to put on. Stampeding inflation – between 1973 and 1975, the cost of such basic theatrical materials as wood and canvas leaped by more than 100 per cent – makes him too expensive to stage any way but his way.

So that, to a certain extent, the centenary gave us a pretext to do what we should have wanted to do anyway. But this time, instead of sharing the cycle among a team of directors, we entrusted them to one man to find his own over-all style and solution for them. What Terry Hands achieved in the centenary season of 1975 is history, and the matter of the rest of this book. In box office terms, it was one of the most successful seasons in our records.

It pleased us, too, to find one of the cheapest seasons we'd mounted in recent years hailed as one of the most spectacular. For that sleight-of-eye we have to thank the brilliance of Farrah. With two simple canopies, one cluster of dead branches and a few dazzling glimpses of gold armour, he hypnotised audiences into listening to the splendour of Shakespeare's words and believing they had seen it.

Thanks in part to the success of that Stratford season, the RSC survived the near squeaks of 1975. With something closer to the confidence of the builders of Stratford's first theatre, it is able to go forward and face the various hair-raising and hair-breadth escapes 1976, 1977, 1978 and 1979 doubtless hold in store for it. After that, our new theatre in the Barbican should be ready, and it will be time to celebrate another milestone in our development with another cycle of histories. Presumably they will need new packaging for that occasion, too. 'The Cheapside Plays', perhaps?

THE INHERITANCE OF HENRY V

SALLY BEAUMAN

There can be few plays that carry upon them more heavily than *Henry V* the weight of centuries of theatrical tradition. That critics have often regarded it as being some aberration of Shakespeare's, a pageant play oddly created when he was at the height of his powers, immediately after the two parts of *Henry IV*, and immediately before *As You Like It* and *Hamlet*, is less surprising when one realises that it was performed *as* a pageant for two hundred years, throughout the eighteenth and most of the nineteenth centuries.

In the eighteenth century, the great tragedians of the day preferred to exercise their talents in *Hamlet*, *Macbeth*, and *Lear*. In the years that Garrick was at Drury Lane–from 1742 to 1776, for instance, *Henry V* was performed on precisely two occasions. It fared slightly better at the rival Covent Garden theatre, because it was a favoured role of two Garden actors–Spranger Barry, and William Smith. If they were there, *Henry V* was performed, if they were not, it was ignored. When it was performed it was staged with as much pomp and circumstance as the budget would allow. Much earlier in the century, in 1723, the tradition of ignoring all Shakespeare's strictures about 'four or five most vile and ragg'd foils' had established itself, with Aaron Hill's production of the play considerably rewritten to allow for an additional love interest, and adapted for maximum spectacle. Hill introduced 'Harriet', a former wronged love of Henry's, and mounted on his stage, pavilions for the French Princess, full-scale bridges, and a cardboard castle of Agincourt. 'After the battle,' announced his programme proudly 'the genius of England arises and sings'.

Spranger Barry and William Smith played in productions which were at least more faithful to the text (though the Chorus was often cut), but they were equally obsessed with spectacle. Smith appeared in the play in 1767, at Covent Garden, and that programme promised the audience breathlessly that as well as the play, '...there will be added the procession from

the *Abbey* at the *Coronation*, with the Representation of
Westminster Hall, and the *Ceremony of the Champion*'
–whatever that was.

The play had rather more revivals towards the end of the
eighteenth century and the beginning of the nineteenth–usually because England was about to go to war
with France. It was given a stirring performance in Manchester
in February 1804, when, yet again threats of invasion from
across the Channel were being met with English defiance.
The alert critic of the *Manchester Townsman* noted on this
occasion that a Mr. Huddard, playing Henry, had altered
the text–as he leapt over the breach, he cried 'God for Harry,
England and King George'. 'Whether', commented the critic,
'this was a lapus linguae, or whether loyalty provoked the
expression, we must leave Mr Huddard to determine...'

Almost throughout the nineteenth century there is little
sign that any theatrical producer thought of *Henry V* as other
than the perfect opportunity to indulge fantasies of Cecil B.
de Mille proportions. Macready closed his last season at
Covent Garden in 1839 with an elaborate production, with
the Chorus restored, but portrayed as 'Time'–'To impress more
strongly upon the audience,' announced the programme notes,
'and to render more palpable those portions of the story,
the narrative and descriptive poetry spoken by the Chorus
is accompanied with Pictorial Illustrations from the pencil
of Mr. Stanfield.' Mr Stanfield's illustrations included
allegorical scenes and a huge diorama of the English fleet
leaving Southampton. The scenery included–inevitably–the
castle of Agincourt, and immense battering rams on wheels.
'We must still maintain an opinion formed long ago,' remarked
The Times coldly, 'that excessive pageantry is no sign of a
revival in the drama.' At the end of Agincourt, another critic
noted 'the actor literally kneels down with his soldiery and
the curtain falls to the solemn strains of an organ, brought
from England, we suppose, for the purpose...'

But *The Times* opinion went unheeded. Twenty years later
Charles Kean staged *Henry V* as his last production at the
Princess's, and spectacle was as strong as ever. Ellen Tree
'recited' the Chorus, in the character of Clio, the Muse of
History, and at the end of her fifth speech, Mr Kean introduced

'An Historical Episode: Old London Bridge, from the Surrey side of the River'. The Episode concerned Henry's triumphant return to London, and the welcoming party that met him, which was 'complete with aldermen, mayor, banners, the tower of London, angels, prophets of a venerable hoariness, dressed in golden coats and singing in sweet harmony, and a chorus of most beautiful virgin girls, elegantly attired in white.'

And so it went on. In 1876 Mr John Coleman staged *Henry V* at the Queen's theatre in a production based as closely as possible on Kean's, including keeping Clio as the Chorus, and inserting numerous tableaux and ballets between the acts. In 1879 Charles Calvert staged the play in London, featuring the march from 'Tancredi' at Harfleur, and excerpts from Verdi's 'Macbeth' at Agincourt. The production was particularly popular because Henry – the matinee idol George Rignold – rode onto the stage every night on a white horse called Crispin.

Henry James went to see it and made precisely the same point as the Chorus: 'Illusion, as such an enterprise proposes to produce it, is absolutely beyond the compass of the stage...' Others were more waspish: 'Who could forget him,' wrote Dutton Cook of George Rignold, 'as, falchion in hand, clothed in complete steel, with a richly emblazoned tabard, he stands in that spot so prized by the histrionic mind, the exact centre of the stage, the limelight pouring down upon him from the flies its most dazzling rays... Of course subtlety of interpretation was not required. Henry V is not an intellectual character.'

That conception of Henry seemed to go hand in hand with the conception of Shakespeare's text as some kind of interlude between the pageants that were the evening's main business. When Richard Mansfield played the part in New York in 1900, the same year that Benson and Waller played it in London, he announced that he had selected the play 'Because of a consideration of its healthy and virile tone... and the lesson it teaches of Godliness, honour, loyalty, courage, cheerfulness and perseverance, its beneficial influence on both old and young.'

The play has been rescued from the grip of spectacle, and Henry himself from a tradition of pious stupidity, largely by the productions of the present century. In 1911 Benson was 'a grave and thoughtful king' who, nevertheless could leap in full armour into the breach. Olivier, with 'his unsparing voice chiselling away at the dead wood of tradition', as J. C. Trewin wrote, played Henry at the Old Vic in 1937. Alec Clunes, Richard Burton, and Ian Holm have all played a major part in the establishment of Henry as a deeper and more complex character. But for a generation, possibly two generations, *Henry V* is still the Olivier film made in 1944 – a production which made many savage cuts, and removed from the hero's mind almost every doubt, and from his path almost every obstacle.

Although the play has always been popular with audiences, it has often been harshly treated by the critics. Johnson found that Shakespeare's 'matter failed him in the fifth act'. Swinburne thought there was no more 'complete incarnation of the militant Englishman, anglais pur sang,' than Henry. Dowden said gently, damning with faint praise, that Henry was perhaps 'Shakespeare's idea of the practical heroic character.' But he wondered, nevertheless, whether this man could be the highest ideal of 'our supreme poet'. Barrett Wendell, an American critic, writing in 1894 thought that Henry was a 'Moral rather than a dramatic hero...rather an ideal than a man, and an ideal, in virtues and vice alike, more British than human.' 'He is after all,' he went on to add, 'not keenly intellectual'. Yeats found Henry a 'ripened Fortinbras', and felt that Shakespeare had given him a rhetoric 'that moves men as a leading article does today.' Shaw thought him simply a 'Jingo hero...an able young Philistine, inheriting high position and authority.' John Masefield, whom one might have expected to like it, thought the play 'bore every mark of being hastily written...it is a chronicle or procession, eked out with soldiers squabbles.'

And so one comes back to the idea of the play as a pageant, an excuse for parades around the stage, and spectacle. And one wonders. Would the play ever have been staged in that way, would scholars and critics have seen it in that way, if the play had not been about England, and an English King? Patriotism has been used so often as an excuse for a production of *Henry V*, that maybe it is that that fogs the play and obscures its issues. Would Macready have staged his spectacles, and would Shaw have so hated this hero, if instead of the 'star of England' he had been perhaps a 'star of Illyria'?

INTRODUCTION TO THE PLAY

TERRY HANDS– DIRECTOR

Sometime in July 1974, after fitful discussion since January of that year, Trevor Nunn, Artistic Director and Chief Executive of the RSC, asked his Planning Committee to vote on his proposal that *Henry IV Part 1*, *Henry IV Part 2*, and *Henry V* should form the back-bone of Company work in 1975, at Stratford. There were eleven votes for the motion and one against. The sole dissenting voice was that of the subsequent Director. During his absence in August *The Merry Wives of Windsor* was added, and by September all four plays had been announced.

The Royal Shakespeare Theatre Centenary Season was launched.

It was a time of economic crisis. National inflation was breaking all records. The Treasury was being called upon to aid industry, and local government. The Arts were necessarily low priority and throughout the country, threatened with curtailment or closure.

The RSC itself was contemplating the loss of the Aldwych, and with it the identity painstakingly built up since 1960. Furthermore the air conditioning and heating system of the Stratford theatre, not good for several years, had finally reached illegal inefficiency. £250,000 had to be found.

The Royal Shakespeare Theatre Centenary Appeal was launched.

In the circumstances it seemed inevitable that we should begin with *Henry V*. First, it is a play of great vitality, with a surging up-beat text: potentially, it has all the impact necessary to herald such a crucial double season. Second it is about improvisation, inter-dependence, and unity: three essential qualities if the company was to surmount its present difficulties.

14

It is not the first time the play has been called upon in such a situation.

In 1945 Laurence Olivier's film had served to stimulate the nation as a whole. The problems of that time were specifically national so the 'patriotic' element in the play was specifically emphasised. From the character of Henry himself all doubt and uncertainty were removed. And so largely the play has been interpreted ever since. However the non-specific unity of 1945, that of armies, is less important to us than the specific unity explored in the play itself: that of individuals aware of their responsibilities, both to themselves and to each other, voluntarily accepting some abdication of that individuality in a final non-hierarchic interdependence – a real brotherhood. And as human unity is more important than national unity and indeed transcends it, so Henry seeks redefinition as 'common-man' before re-assuming his function as King. It is an agonising re-appraisal on any level.

Consequently the doubts and uncertainties inherent in the role of Henry might be re-admitted.

The play is full of doubt. Full of uncertainty. And it begins with an admission of failure. The Chorus apologises that the theatre is too small, too impoverished, too limited properly to bring forth the story of Henry V. He calls upon the imagination of the audience to supplement that of the 'flat unraised spirits', so that together, working, they may collaborate in an act of creation – called *Henry V.*

It is a statement quintessential to all theatre, but especially relevant to us. As the Chorus bemoans the passing of spectacular masque theatre, so may we regret the passing of lavish proscenium theatre; as he regrets a small company, so we miss the marching tread of spear carriers; as he ruefully indicates a wooden O so we deplore our wooden □. Or do we? And does he?

No, not really. At last under the protective umbrella of financial stricture – protection only from the critics incidentally – we could abandon the artistic strictures of 'naturalist' theatre, with its cinematic crowds and group reactions, and focus on each actor as an individual. We could reduce the conflict of text and decor, and trust in the ability of wooden floors, square or oval, to transform themselves from boards into billows at a leap of the audience's imagination. With relief we decided to start from rehearsal clothes and a rehearsal situation. We felt we were doing what many people in the theatre had been longing to do for years. Start from scratch. And as the dictionary for this new method was specifically provided by the Chorus soliloquy, so we arrived at the fundamental reason for beginning with *Henry V*.

It is Shakepeare's theatre play par excellence. Every aspect of role playing is examined. The costume, the make-up, the internal performance, the external. The roles played in public and the roles played in private. It is no new theme. It runs throughout the plays: from Jacques': 'All the world's a stage;' to Lear's: 'When we are born we cry that we are come/To this great stage of fools'. In the '*Henries*' it is particularly focused. The politician Bolingbroke, acting the King. Hal acting robber, drawer, barrister, king, Falstaff, roisterer, son, King. Both struggling to find an identity. A personal identity in a traditional world.

And those personal identities are further re-examined through the love and competition and language difficulties of the father-son relationship: Hal and Henry IV, Hotspur and Northumberland; together with a host of surrogate father relationships: Hotspur and Worcester, Hotspur and Glendower, Young Mortimer and Glendower, Mowbray and the Archbishop of York, Hal and Falstaff, Hal and the Lord Chief Justice. In *Henry IV Part One* the fathers manipulate the sons; in *Part Two*, like spring after winter, the sons replace the fathers. 'And herein will I imitate the sun' says Hal in *Part One*. He is prepared to 'act' the son, and the sun-king. Personal responsibility for the function conferred by Richard II's 'hollow-crown' is the path he examines in his *Part Two* soliloquy. It leads to the acted majesty of 'a rich armour worn in heat of day/That scalds with safety'–his end of *Part Two* coronation. But as the role becomes intolerable so too does its performance. Both will need redefinition in *Henry V*.

In *Henry V* all the themes come together within the basic

theatrical metaphor. And as *Henry V* contains *Henry IV Parts One* and *Two* again it may readily precede them.

Hal, as King, is an unknown quantity, so too, at the start of the evening is the actor playing the role. They should both be rehearsing. Rehearsal is a period of experimental communication. As is acting. Whether the Bank Manager sits amid oak, steel, and concrete to suggest security, or the young lady defies nature and sometimes gravity with foundation garments–they are all only support systems for communication. If you ever did hold Hamlet's mirror up to nature, all you'd see would be another series of mirrors.

Communication–'Why?' 'How?', and result, became the essence of every rehearsal.

Within the 'why' we could examine political motive: the Archbishop defending his gold, Henry his claim to the throne. (The play can hardly be called chauvinist incidentally when it so elaborately reveals that the two ruling houses of England and France, Angevin and Valois, are in fact related and both descended from the Danes; the English by way of the Normans, also Scandinavian. And Henry later compounds the confusion by claiming he is Welsh.)

We could examine personal motive: the Dauphin's longing to escape the strictures of the French court, Hal assessing the need for personal redefinition, in action.

Within the 'how' we could explore the technique of utterance–the language of role-playing: the Archbishop terse and private with Ely, elaborate and longwinded with the King. Henry earnest and concerned, remembering the northern incursions of *Henry IV Part One*, then publicly with the grandiloquent phrases of formal challenge, cannon bullets for tennis balls, assuming experimentally the 'port of Mars'. The result of that communication precipitates a mixed bag of Island types into an equally mixed bag of Continent types. The process why, how and result endlessly regenerating the next stage of character and narrative evolution.

In rehearsal little was imposed save perhaps the concept of the 'breach'. There was no 'blocking' until the last week of rehearsals and then it was simply a temporary fixing of the movements generally agreed. Everything was limited to speaking and listening. We explored direct delivery–using the audience as a kind of telephone exchange through which conversation might be passed–an old technique re-applied. But if the audiences were really to participate imaginatively then they had to become actors *within* the spectacle. We were only 24, they might be 1500 per night–all the armies one could ever hope for, provided they too were rehearsed–even in absentia.

We tried to be as simple as possible.

'Shouldn't we all cheer here'

'No. We shouldn't *all* do anything. You cheer if you want to'

'But we're supposed to be an army.'

'Yes. But you *are* seven people'

'So we don't cheer.'

'So you *do* cheer–if you want to.'

'What about the others?'

'They'll cheer if *they* want to'.

'But if I cheer on my own, I'll look silly'

'You're playing Pistol.'

The principle of direct communication covered every motive, every action, and provided its own discipline. It liberated the cast from 'reactions'. They spoke to the sentence rather than the parenthesis; they discovered syntax and abandoned 'colour'. In the general acceleration we found we could play much more of the text than usual. And the more text we played the more remarkable the play became. The 'why-how-result' process followed the natural, revealed rhythm of the play itself. An alternating pattern of doubt and certainty.

The play begins in failure. It continues in doubt. Should Henry attack France? Should he consolidate at home, embarking upon a programme of social welfare using Church money and thereby continuing the modernisation begun by his father? Remember that Henry VIII's reign was in living memory of some of Shakespeare's own generation. Church money would provide external redress. But would the spirit be touched? Does the country need pragmatic solutions, or inspiration? Is Henry to be a mediaeval or a renaissance king?

He appeals to yet another surrogate father–and receives blandishments and self-interest in reply. He is aware of the urge to action among his immediate family–brothers, uncle, cousin–but to leave his new kingdom so soon? Will not the Scots invade? How are his people? Indeed who *are* his people? He has mixed with high and low as Hal, probably more than any other king since Alfred. And what he has seen has not been reassuring. Perhaps to get them all together in one observable place is the only solution. And so his 'war' is born.

But war in this sense is less 'war-mongering' than Shakespeare's dramatic pretext for assembling the elements of Henry's nation–in one place, at one time, for examination. The metaphor serves to contrast the imposed unity of mediaeval discipline with the agreed unity of interdependence. If he can unite his 'army', he will unite his 'country'.

Henry, in true Hal fashion, is to re-assume his favourite role of observer. But now for the first time he will, as King, be the 'observed of all observers'–more than he realises and more than he wishes.

With so much uncertain, so much in a rehearsal stage, it seemed only reasonable that initially the presentation should be indeterminate also; rehearsal lighting, rehearsal clothes. As Henry lifts into decision, the first costume arrives on stage, the lights come up. The Chorus carries the new certainty and cues the first music. Then the first demonstration of stage-spectacle: a heraldic canopy, a cannon–'Now all the youth of England are on fire'. The actors rush into costume. Only to be undercut by Corporal Nym, who doesn't want to go to war, keeps his sword for toasting cheese, and limits his political vision to Quickly's petticoats. From hot to cold; and back to hot again, as Bardolph, Nym and Pistol battle over Mistress Quickly, money, size, and anything else they can think of, save the matter in question–war with France–which they never think of. It is another style of acting, deliberately music-hall and front cloth. Shared between two groups of spectators, the audience and the rest of the cast on stage still dressing for war. At its hottest point, the arrival of the Boy, Francis, with news of Falstaff's illness, plunges the scene into doubt again.

The Chorus continues the mood of insecurity. At Southampton the traitors Scroop, Cambridge and Grey await Henry. Exactly as Henry feared, the country is too recently at peace to forget the squabbles and betrayals of his father's reign. Before even leaving England he has cause to regret his decision. He deals with the traitors, but the explosions of passion provided by Shakespeare witness an appalled insecurity. Betrayed politically and personally, who now *can* he trust? And how many more Yorkist or French or Scottish or Welsh sympathisers are waiting for his absence to throw the country back into the civil strife his father gave his life to eradicate:

> *For all my reign hath been but as a scene*
> *Acting that argument.*

He is alone and from the low point of that solitude forces himself into the responsibility of leadership. He accepts the banner-surcoat of 'patriotism', he re-asserts the 'glory' of conquest. Astride the cannon, sword in hand, singing with his troops, he 'acts' the role of warrior-king. Only we, who know the fire he has passed through, can judge what that performance costs him. It is a brave but insecure paean. It solves nothing. We plunge all the more easily into the death of Falstaff, which reiterates and re-echoes the sense of loss, felt at the end of *Henry IV Part Two* and again after Southampton. Pistol takes the lead, his confident:

> *Let us to France; like horse-leeches, my boys,*
> *To suck, to suck, the very blood to suck.*

– sweeps the mercury back up the thermometer. The arrival of the French in Scene six sends it back into the bulb.

They are civilised, distant. Unwilling to fight, insecure, full of foreboding. Only the Dauphin, young, excitable, sees in battle the chance to escape the peace time etiquette of an antiquated court. Like Henry, but more naively, he wants change. A personal, rather than hierarchic, identity. For him too, 'war' is not patriotic, nor an end in itself, but the means to a personal realisation. He has played the son too long. His clash with the sardonic Exeter puts the play back into war-gear, and the Chorus maintains the mood, back-tracking, re-emphasising the elation, the superficial confidence of embarkation. He leads us to the very gates of Harfleur. And at last this 'patriotic tub-thumping, jingoistic, fascist, over-confident, war-mongering, chronicle' explodes into action.

And the English are in retreat.

The irony is staggering.

And so it has been from the beginning and so it will continue.

I really cannot see how this play has earned its unflattering epithets. There is enough in it to satisfy every pacifist, warrior, poet, peasant, scientist and sectarian ever invented. And yet perversely the superb text is ignored–the contradictions, the complexities, the sheer Shakespearianess of it all–and Shakespeare in full control of his powers at that. I can only conclude that for some obscure reason all the above have ignored the bits directed at them, and only looked at the bits directed at others. And you find it everywhere: in conversation, in scholarly tomes, in the press. Especially in the press. You might as well condemn *Lear* as geriatric fantasy, or *Twelfth Night* as bisexual banality. But not even Tolstoy or Shaw have been as prejudiced as the latter day assessors of *Henry V.* The play is by Shakespeare, for goodness sake! Nothing is ever what is seems. Ever.

Henry re-inspires his shattered army. It is a key moment. A soliloquy.

The personal example he sets is straight forward and of no special interest. We have seen him at Shrewsbury, we know he can rise to this occasion. What is interesting is the way he re-inspires his men. The 'how' of his communication. He uses all the words of pretence, all the words of theatre. He encourages an external performance, that may lead to an internal: 'imitate', 'disguise', 'copy'. He is supported by the Chorus, who just before has appealed yet again for our patience: 'And eke out our performance with your mind'. Reminding us again that we are in a theatre watching a play. We have come to see a performance. We study all the more keenly the performance Henry gives. It is splendid. He accepts the responsibility of leadership. He leads. But the separation is still marked in his speech between 'you noblest English' and 'good yeoman'. It is a convincing performance. It convinces everybody except Pistol, Bardolph, Nym and the Boy. From Henry's high heroism we descend to their low pragmatism. 'The knocks are too hot'.

They are the first 'separatist group' of the play. Landless, lawless, parasites on the body-politic and personal. Falstaff has endlessly tried to banish them in *Parts One* and *Two*. They give nothing, they do nothing. They take, they steal. And as the boy points out, they want him to steal too–not for himself, but for them. They are the last remnants of Falstaff's alternative government. Pimps to a new age not part of it. And like Falstaff they must go.

Yet they are likeable.

And they sing.

The second 'separatist' group is introduced. The four captains from England, Wales, Scotland and Ireland. Where the first group is united in self-interest, the second is disunited in self-obsession. Where the former's language is a parody of Henry's rhetoric, the latter parody language altogether. The four captains no more understand one another than Young Mortimer does Glendower's daughter, or Davey, Bardolph or Henry IV, Hal.

We have further acting styles. 'Mechanicals' followed by 'comics', following 'rhetorics'. Somehow Henry must weld these disparate groups together spiritually, as the play must stylistically.

But still he opts for externals. The speech to the Governor of Harfleur again emphasises appearance: 'array'd in flames' 'smirched complexion'–Henry goes on to create a vocal scenario of traditional warfare. The more he speaks, the more possible it becomes. We know such things exist in human nature. So does Henry. Right from the beginning his has been the only voice reminding us that war is not glory but misery and bloodshed. Again he voices his reminder, and emphasises the attendant horrors. If Harfleur resists the performance will continue, and the consequence will be inevitable. Henry will be trapped in his role–as he was trapped in his coronation finery at the end of *Henry IV Part Two*. And should he play it out, the deed will condemn him to the part of Pyrrhus, for ever. The pressure is immense.

Again Shakespeare undercuts. The Governor surrenders.

The deflation of tension is marked by Henry's tears of relief. He confides to Exeter and so to us, that beneath the bravado was the knowledge of sickness in his own army. The knowledge that he must retreat. The knowledge of failure.

Having begun in doubt and uncertainty we now return to it. Henry has failed. He has won a battle and lost the war. His achievement is negligible, his army quarrelling, or mutinous. His solitude intense. And at this point Shakespeare chooses to remind him of what he's been missing. He introduces the French princess Katherine and her lady Alice.

Hal has inhabited a totally male world. It has been a harsh world, with little quarter and less warmth. He survives Shrewsbury but loses the confrontation with Doll Tearsheet. The relationships he does form, crumble as they are achieved, Hotspur and Henry IV both die at the moment of understanding. Now the first unattached marriageable female in three plays is introduced. The scene is very sexual, very feminine: Shakespeare picks up several themes: that of language, that of communication. With Ludmila Mikaël sociétaire of the Comédie Française, we were able to add another – a different acting style. The élan and panache of French theatre challenging the detail and tonic freedom of English.

The French stung by Harfleur, call up their full chivalry. Shakespeare writes a perfect 'tirade'. A massive army is launched against Henry's dispirited band.

Again the play is high.

And again it swoops from trumpeting French glory to English despair. Henry arrives to good news – the Duke of Exeter, his uncle, has succeeded in holding a bridgehead against the French. Fluellen announces: 'the perdition of the enemy has been very great' but that no Englishman has been killed. Shakespeare forces our attention upon the one Englishman who will be – Bardolph – the companion of Falstaff, friend of Hal's youth. His death is obviously felt. Nym, a comparative newcomer, is disposed of in two lines later in the play. Here Shakespeare takes nearly fifty – insisting again and again upon an exact physical description. Henry is forced to uphold his own laws, his own beliefs. The observer now observed, he must be seen to be impartial. The indulgence of Gadshill is savagely repaid. However likable, Bardolph *must* go. But why now? The army is in retreat–all hopes of conquest gone. Why not leave it till tomorrow, when all will die anyway? Amidst the doubt and uncertainty facing him Henry chooses again the way of instinct. Neither he nor Shakespeare are sentimental. It shows a greater courage than the breach, a greater maturity than the reply to the Dauphin. Montjoy's arrival, his offer of ransom, harshly emphasise the lesson of Bardolph's death. Once committed Henry cannot draw back. He drops his 'acting', he admits to the truth of his situation. He throws in *his* life with that of his soldiers. He cannot hope for victory, only dignity. He kicks and pushes his 'poore souldiers' into further effort. They have all reached their lowest point.

The night scenes are the natural consequence of the despair of Scene twelve. Henry's way is guided and prepared by the Chorus, whose friendly irony has provided Hal with the father he so significantly lacked in *Parts One* and *Two*–a role taken supremely by Emrys James, carrying his identity on from the power and practicality of his revelatory Bolingbroke. Henry talks to his men. First as 'Welshman', with Pistol, then in the cloak of yet another father-figure, Sir Thomas Erpingham, then as common-man, with common-men. Again Shakespeare allows us to look at his separate groups: the 'mechanicals'–now only Pistol and the Boy, the 'comics'–Fluellen and Gower and introduces a kind of private soldiery–Williams, Bates and Court. Listening to them, talking to them, arguing with them, Henry refines his idea of individual personal responsibility. It leads into the third great soliloquy of the composite Hal/Henry role. He confronts Kingship and public responsibility–its torment, its barreness. He strips it bare of theatrical adornment–make-up, costume, decor–with all its attendant behaviour. He finds it has no separate identity. Like a long-lived nightmare he finds at last that it doesn't exist. There is no king or kingship. Only Henry himself. He passes through his blackest and most obscure moment. Striking bargains, like a child, with a further father-figure–God. As absent as all the others.

It is a personal revelation. A personal exorcism. Henry leaves the stage no longer 'King' yet never more 'Kingly'.

The first note of confidence enters his voice: 'The day, my friends, and all things stay for me'.
He has found himself. Henry IV didn't achieve such self-awareness until his death-bed. Henry V has at least a new day.

The play is not really about war. But it does contain three battles. They increase in importance.
The first is Harfleur, fought from externals, revealing the deep divisions in Henry's army and consequently his country. The second is Agincourt, fought by a renewed and re-united band of brothers. Henry's self awareness touches that of his fellows. He abandons privilege and rank, the final offer of ransom. He awakens interdependence and trust, he speaks to all as equals, and accepts equality with them for himself. Above all Shakespeare's theatre lesson has gone within:

> *By Jove, I am not covetous for gold,*
> *Nor care I who doth feed upon my cost;*
> *It yearns me not if men my garments wear;*
> *Such outward things dwell not in my desires:*

Even the externals of performance are no longer necessary. 'All things are ready if our minds be so'. It is the same message uttered by the Chorus at the beginning of the play. It will serve for visual spectacle, or personal behaviour. It has taken both parts of *Henry IV* and the majority of *Henry V* to get there. It becomes the real point of the victory at Agincourt.
The battle itself with Pistol, the Boy, Le Fer, is clownesque, symbolic and unimportant to the larger issues. Except perhaps that battles are better fought by fools than real human beings. It turns on ransom and serves more to show the outmoded concepts of the French than the valour of the English. It is obviously significant to Shakespeare's irony that after so much, 'militarism' the famous 'battle' is fought by two cowards and a child. For those who *like* war plays it is a frustrating climax. More frustration is to follow in Henry's third and most important battle. The courtship of Katherine.

It is a part of the play often criticised. But like the last act of *The Merchant of Venice* it is more important, I suspect, to Shakespeare than all that has gone before. It is a romantic nineteenth century vision, which stops at the soldiering of Agincourt or the obviousness of Shylock's trial. To Shakespeare, and probably his audience, life is always more important than death. And it requires its own act. Henry tries all his old roles, boy, bluff soldier, king. None of them fool the instinctive feminine wisdom of the French princess. She has learnt his language, now he must learn hers. Shakespeare's themes come together. Himself a son, Henry will now become father. He does speak French–finally, and correctly. It is the turning point of the scene. They fall in love, as themselves, as equals. They achieve nature's best garden and of it leave their son imperial lord.

Henry V is a remarkably structured play. From the doubts at the beginning to the confidence of the great wooing scene, it is, like so many of Shakepeare's plays, a superbly balanced allegory. Though that word starts so many hares, we may be safer to call it a poem.

We talk so much about Shakespeare's poetry that I feel we often forget how limited our real view of that poetry is. There are endless discussions about metre, and stopped lines, parenthesis, colour. Yet all those discussions seem to remain at one level, that of the line itself. It has been said that the tragedy of *Macbeth* is that of a warrior-poet. Why? Because he kills and speaks poetry. By that token Shakespeare's plays are entirely peopled by grave-diggers, hostesses etc. all inhabiting asylums for the peculiarly gifted.

But surely this is not the case. He creates real people, talking really, *within* a poem. There is poetry in structure, in juxtaposition, in rhythm. A poem is communication through image–and it is an ambiguous communication at that. Each individual image defies analysis, and together they add up, not to a thesis but to an experience. The ambiguity is intentional. The less it is explained by decor and costume, the greater is its richness. Whatever else we attempted or achieved in the production of *Henry V*, everything–rehearsals, staging, performance–was aimed at communicating its poetry. Not just the spoken line, but the real poetry of the whole. The golden armour of the French, Henry's armour for his coronation in *Part Two*, the follow spots, Farrah's canopies, Guy's music, the empty stage, the actors changing styles and utterance, all were images within the overall poem. The wooing scene is the climax of the poem and therefore the real climax to the play.

And *Henry V* is the actor who plays the title role. It is his play. Therefore his production. The unique distinction of Alan Howard's performance was his endless sensitivity to that poetry, his constant reflection of that poem.

Together we tried to build a ladder of images toward the experience made available by Shakespeare. We couldn't analyse it then, we can't now. Sooner ask a termite its assessment of a violin.

THE INTERVIEWS

THE DESIGNER

FARRAH

Q: The first thing that strikes anyone who goes regularly to Stratford, and who enters the theatre to see *Henry V,* is that you have radically altered the appearance of the stage itself. Why and how did you do that?

Farrah: The idea for the staging we used came about because *Henry V* was the first play of the season. I thought about the opening words of the Chorus, the 'unworthy scaffold', the 'cockpit', the 'wooden O', and I felt that what we wanted to create was not a box of illusions, but something that freed the audience's imaginations and made them conjure their own illusions. And, because we were beginning the play as if the actors were rehearsing, we wanted an area that was clearly defined, but which also could be seen to be an organic part of the building that everyone – actors and the audience – were part of. So we stripped the stage; we cleared it of everything extraneous, to make it as austere and as bare as possible. The proscenium arch was clad – boxed in: we took all that away so that you could see the bare brick. The back wall of the stage had never been seen before, it had always been covered by flats or drapes. We got rid of them. The wall itself was covered in old gas pipes and electrical fittings. We took them all down. We painted the proscenium arch and the walls throughout in off-white paint, and we built a new stage-platform with a one-in-twelve rake. It was a stage designed to launch the actors into the audience. The comment that pleased me most was that it was like the great deck of an aircraft carrier. It meant that the actors on the stage were very clearly defined, and that they too were metaphorically stripped. They had none of the usual comforting stage accoutrements. I think it meant that those who were good were better than usual, and those who were average were killed. It wasn't a stage where you could hide weakness.

Q: You didn't use any traditional masking, did you?

Farrah: No, I wanted all the working trimmings of a stage to be clearly visible – the lamps, the bridges. One wanted the

31

audience, and the actors to feel, 'OK here are all the essentials for the beginning of a theatrical performance–now, let's start the story, and make the illusion begin.'

Q: Why did you use the canopies as you did?

Farrah: I wanted to concentrate on one spectacular theatrical device, which was very adaptable, very flexible, and could be put to use all through the play. And the canopies were that: the first canopy could suddenly open up over the stage, a beautiful, heraldic, glorious roof over the heads of the actors. It could provide exactly the feeling that a modern audience expects when it goes to see a play about the kings of England, and yet it was more than that. It couldn't be placed, finally, in any neat context–it looked baroque, and yet it also looked Asiatic–the rest of the stage was so austere that the effect of the canopy was like those exquisite carpets, or the single piece of material that you see in Chinese or Japanese theatre. But it was organic also, to the whole play: that beautiful roof over the characters' heads could descend for the war scenes, and become the world under their feet–a muddy field in France. And the second canopy, which appears for the last scene, was different. It was gold, but it looked textured, a little like lungs; it didn't assert as the first heraldic canopy does, but it seemed right for the reconciliation in the French court.

Q: Was there any specific thing which triggered the idea for the canopies?

Farrah: It was a number of things. Whenever Terry and I work on a production we spend a long time just looking at photographs, and at books. They may not necessarily have anything to do with the theatre, or the play in hand. We looked at photographs of battles–Verdun–and at pictures of people putting up circus tents. They were sessions full of bewilderment, but something emerged from them. Also, I had done a production of Brecht's *Man is Man* on the continent, which was performed in a circus tent, and I had watched that tent being set up and struck. All those things. And of course, the need always at the back of my mind to find a strong theatrical statement, which meant something in the context of the play.

Q: How were the canopies made?

Farrah: They're made of the same material as circus tents–cotton duck. The multicoloured heraldic signs were sewn on to the underside. The material has the effect of looking very light, very billowy, but in fact it's not–it's just the way it's hung.

Q: When the canopy goes down, and becomes the fields of France, and everything on the stage is grey and brown–it has the effect of making Henry's war in France curiously timeless. It could be the Somme, D day, almost any war. And that is emphasized by the costumes of the English soldiers. Did you want that feeling in those scenes?

Farrah: Yes I did. We knew that we were working with only a small cast–there were not twenty extras at our disposal. So I felt that we had to hit on an image of war that was familiar to everyone in the audience, that each of them would recognise. I wanted the feeling of a small group of men who had had to improvise for survival, and I wanted it to have the feeling of *all* wars–of Napoleon's retreat from Moscow, of Stalingrad, of the Marne. I think once an army is in that kind of situation, fighting to live, they look the same in any century. Misery and desperation reduce them to much the same physical state.

Q: But the French are in complete contrast to this?

Farrah: Yes. With the French I wanted to show people who were extremely civilised, extremely sophisticated–very beautiful. People who were bound to be obliterated. I based their costumes in the court scenes very much on books of fifteenth century French miniatures, and in particular an extraordinary book–the *Coeur d'Amour Epris*, which is written by René d'Anjou, and which is filled with the most marvellous paintings.

Q: What about the French on the battlefield, in the armour they're so proud of?

Farrah: The only way that you could make a contrast in that world of mud–greys and browns and pale faces–was to use a very neat shape that reflects the light. I wanted a sense of people who are untouched by the realities of war, even when they're in a tent on a battlefield, because that makes their sacrifice all the more telling. We made their armour gold, because it is rich and shiny, and dehumanising. They're encased in it; they have no contact with the ordinary men who are sick and exhausted and miserable.

Q: It links too, doesn't it, with the image of Henry that you have given us, at his coronation at the end of *Henry IV Part Two?* You chose to make him wear golden armour rather than conventional coronation robes.

Farrah: Yes. I wanted people to see a Henry who was unreachable, untouchable. Quite beyond the appeal of Falstaff and the others.

Q: Your design for the French very much accords with Terry Hands' conception of them. Were you in agreement over that from the beginning, or was it an idea that emerged when you first began talking about the play?

Farrah: I think we agreed on the difference between the French and the English in the play from the first. We both felt that the turning point of the play was Agincourt, and how one nation, with its back to the wall could defeat a powerful and beautiful civilisation. I know more about French history than about English, so I had to do some homework – but that has advantages. You come up with some odd things that can be very interesting. Terry always says that if they're too odd he can always blame the fact that he has an Arab designer.

Q: What about the breach scene? I think one of the most exciting moments in the production is when that great wall suddenly rises up from the floor of the stage.

Farrah: Well, I wanted to use all the resources of the stage that we had. And there was a huge network of lifts that had been installed for the Romans season. We didn't have that much money available, and so anything that could be used had to be. What I wanted was something that would give the audience a sense of danger – which I think it did because it was so steeply raked. And something which the actors could use which was slightly dangerous for them also – something they would need to be acrobatic to cope with, but which would not hinder the delivery of their lines. I was helped in that respect a lot by Alan Howard – because he was excited by it, and wanted to work on it. It's very good when you get that kind of response from actors.

Q: A lot of actors criticise designers, of course, for imposing things on them and then expecting them to carry a scene weighted down with 'design statements'. Do you try consciously to listen to the actors' point of view?

Farrah: Well, plays like the histories are not easy for actors from the costume point of view. They're used to walking around in sandals and blue jeans, and suddenly they have to act in all this gear. But they must wear it. The characters in these plays have to look monumental; when they fight they must look heavy, they must wield massive weapons. And in these productions the deliberate lack of scenery meant that the actors had to appear in a very definite way. But if an actor is not convinced by what he's wearing it's no good. That's why fittings are so important. They have to be squeezed in between rehearsals, but they give the actor a chance to say what he feels about something when there's still time to change it.

Q: What about money? There has been a certain amount of criticism of the RSC, even from within the company, for overspending on design. Did you have to work within a tight budget, and if you did, did you mind?

Farrah: We had an overall budget figure from the management. But we kept constantly revising the breakdown of that figure because costs of everything rocketed so fast as we were working. And a lot of things one needs are difficult to come by now—it isn't easy to get the right kind of steel for swords, it isn't even that easy to get armour made. A lot of the armour we used was old stuff, tarted up. There were a lot of complications, and we came in under budget.

Sometimes I mind about financial restrictions; if you work for some West End managements for instance now, they want a designer, but they don't want him to spend any money. Which can be a little frustrating. You have to refrain from doing things that you know are right and you know would be exciting. I didn't feel that at Stratford. Sometimes restrictions can turn out to be very liberating.

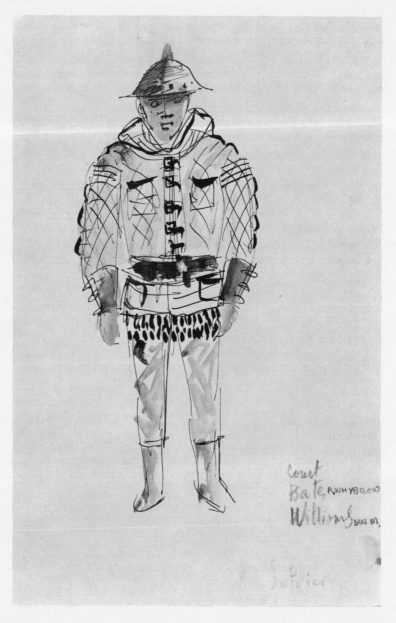

An archer in the English Army

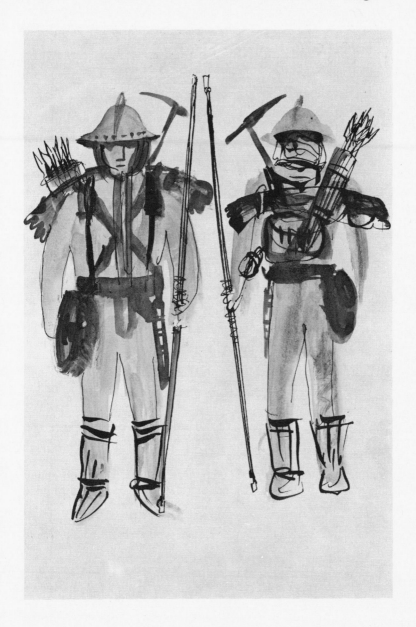

Archers in the English army

Bardolph–played by Tim Wylton

The Dauphin,-played by Geoffrey Hutchings

Macmorris, the Irish captain–played by Barrie Rutter

Pistol–played by Richard Moore

The Boy–played by Peter Bourke

Henry V, in full armour – played by Alan Howard

H.V.—D

The French Knights in their Agincourt armour. Orleans–played by Philip
Dunbar; The Constable of France, played by Bernard Brown; The Dauphin,
played by Geoffrey Hutchings.

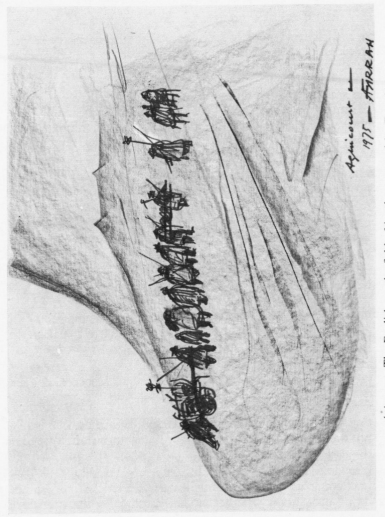

Agincourt—The English on the field of battle as staged by Farrah.

THE COMPOSER

GUY WOOLFENDEN

Q: You had worked on the music for *Henry V* before–for Peter Hall's production with Ian Holm in 1964. Was it difficult to start work on the play again, for a different production, with, presumably, a different vision of the play?

Guy Woolfenden: It wouldn't have been difficult if I hadn't liked the music I originally wrote. But unfortunately I did. I was pleased with it. I thought it was very good. And that particular 1964 production had been around for a long time too: it was revived several times after the original production; it was adapted into a slightly different *Theatre-go-round* production. The music I wrote for it just lived with me for rather a long while. So it *was* difficult this time. It was very hard to get what I'd written before out of my head. When I read the play again I found that certain words, which had been music cues in the earlier production immediately brought the piece of music I wrote to go with them leaping into my head. I only had to read the words 'minding true things by what their mockeries be', and all the sounds of yesteryear flooded back. However, not a single note of music in this production is the same as in the previous one–except for the sound-montage of the battle of Agincourt–so I suppose I must have managed it.

Q: How do you begin writing the music for a production like this? You must have to talk the play over endlessly with the other people involved in working on it.

Guy Woolfenden: Well, one finds oneself mouthing the phrase, but the collaborative effort *is* every bit as important as reading the text. I couldn't have begun to work on this play without knowing Terry's ideas about the play, and Abdel's. Until Abdel had come up with the catwalks at the side of the stage I didn't even know whether we had a place to put musicians. Until Terry had told me how the opening sequences of the play were going to be done–in actors' ordinary clothes, as if at a rehearsal–I couldn't decide how and when to start the music. The first music cue in this production is twenty minutes into the play; in the previous production there had already been several music cues–the whole play had begun with tuckets, with heraldic music.

Q: The music for the opposing sides in the war–the English and the French–very much reinforces Terry Hands' ideas about them. How did you and he work on that?

Guy Woolfenden: Terry and I had long discussions about the play, and about the differences on the two sides. The English are a small expeditionary force; they've crossed the Channel; they've flogged their way to Harfleur, and have gone into retreat. The French are rich and sophisticated, extremely civilised and extremely powerful. I wanted very simple gentle music for the first French court scenes–for which I used harps, for instance–and I wanted colossal fierce music for the French King's speech when he summons the French nobles to make war on England. I wanted there to be a feeling then, of the French war machine rolling and rumbling into action. For the English I wanted something jaunty, natural, that the soldiers could whistle if they felt like it. I was thinking of things like the film *The Bridge on the River Kwai*: you know how they used the *Colonel Bogie* march in that film? Now everyone knows it's a march, and there are lots of scurrilous words to it, but the fact that the men in the film *whistled* it made it very moving. That sort of thing can be over-sentimentalised, but I think there is something that has gone on in our national subconscious for centuries, that can best be summed up by the term 'British Tommy'. I felt that the British going off to war with France were not very different from the British Expeditionary force in the Great War, or the soldiers at the Normandy landings. And I wanted a feeling in their music of all those whistled soldiers' tunes–*Lilli Marlene, It's a Long Way to Tipperary....*

Q: There is one English tune, isn't there–the *Deo Gracias* marching tune, which is used several times in the production. It's used when they march off to war from Southampton; Henry forces the men to sing it when they march away from the bridge at the end of the first half of the play, when all the soldiers are mutinous and fed up; it's used again when they leave the field of battle after the reading of the dead of Agincourt. How did you work on that piece of music?

Guy Woolfenden: There's a long story to that tune. We had a lot of trouble with it. Terry originally asked me for a march for the end of the Southampton scene, and he suggested that it should have words. Now that immediately gets you into a very dodgy area: finding a poem, if you like, that the Bard didn't provide. Directors and musicians tend to get cold feet. Terry and I have avoided it in the past: when we did *Pericles*, for instance, we used Latin texts, which weren't likely to offend an audience, because no-one understood them. But it wouldn't have been particularly apposite if the entire English army had suddenly burst into Latin, so that was out.

I found a marvellous fifteenth century poem, in praise of Henry and his victories. It was a macaronic poem, which means it sandwiches the vernacular with Latin, and the refrain of it was *Deo Gracias*. But the words to the rest of it were inappropriate because they were all about how Henry had defeated the French at Agincourt, and when we wanted to use it in the production they hadn't even embarked from England. I then found another poem, and wrote a tune for it. Terry liked the tune; nobody liked the words, and I'm now the only person who remembers them. And it was at that point that we decided to use this tune, with the soldiers just whistling it, which was a feeling I wanted, and to keep the refrain *Deo Gracias*. And it adapts, according to how its played and sung, or whistled, to the feeling on stage at that particular moment. It's very cheerful at Southampton; very forced and unwilling at the bridge, after the death of Bardolph. And after the reading of the dead it's something else again. At that moment in the play Shakespeare makes Henry say 'Let there be sung Non Nobis, and Te Deum.' I had written a *Non Nobis* for the previous production which I couldn't get out of my head, and that caused some problems. We resolved it finally by having Fluellen, the bookish man of the play, begin by singing a proper plain-song *Te Deum*, and the English army gradually and irrepressibly beginning to hum their marching tune. And I think that works very well, it is very sad, but also very warm, and completely understandable, after what has just happened to them. The same tune is also used very softly, under Emrys James' voice, at the very end of the play, when it's played pianissimo on woodwind. And it comes in, with full brass, as he finishes the last speech.

Q: You mentioned the presence of the musicians earlier. Do you prefer to use live music rather than tapes?

Guy Woolfenden: Well, we are using a wide variety of instruments in the play. There is a flute doubling piccolo; an oboe doubling cor anglais; a bassoon; two trumpets; a harp; a trombone; and two horns — they play both ordinary orchestral horns, and French open hunting horns, which have a much more braying, aggressive quality. Finally there are two percussion players, on either side of the stage, at the back, one who plays tympani, kettledrums and so on, and the other who has a vast array of about twenty different percussion instruments. There is no way that you could get the same quality of sound that they produce by using tapes. Apart from the technical difficulties with speakers, it always sounds canned. And tapes are much less versatile. It's very difficult to use taped music within a speech, for instance. If you have live music during a speech, and an actor misses out a line, or alters his phrasing and pace, the musician can keep with him; a tape can't.

Q: What do you want the music to contribute to a production like this one?

Guy Woolfenden: In nearly every Shakespeare play that I write music for, there are two sorts of music. There is music *of* the play, and music *about* the play. The first category is simple — it's music that is called for directly in the text by one of the characters — so that when Henry says, for instance, 'Take a trumpet, herald,' or when the Constable says 'Then let the trumpets sound/The tucket sonance, and the note to mount', then clearly a trumpet call is needed. The music is not commenting on the action, it is as much a part of the play as the words. The second category, music *about* the play is perhaps closer to film music, it helps to set up a certain mood that is right for a particular scene or moment. In this production, for instance, there is a lot of music under speech, which is quite rare in the theatre — like the music played very softly under the last Chorus speech, that I mentioned earlier. And there is music punctuating speech, which can have the effect of heightening the text considerably. When the French King summons up that great list of the French nobles to war — less reverently known as the French wine list — his speech is punctuated by great braying calls from the French hunting horns, which makes the king seem gigantic and terrifying, and helps to build the speech to a huge climax on 'And quickly bring us word of England's fall.' It's very difficult to get that kind of thing exactly right; the spirit has to be right, and the execution has to be exact. The musicians playing the horns have their cue words written on to the music, so that the whole speech is like a musical score.

But there are lots of quieter moments than that, where I use music, and the audience is probably hardly aware of it, but it helps the mood of the scene enormously. There are signal trumpets off stage, for instance, which call each other all through the night in the English scenes before the battle. They help to re-inforce the feeling of doom in the scene, and they are like clocks–they mark the passing hours of this endlessly long night.

Q: I was reading an account recently of a nineteenth century production of *Henry V* in which organ music was used during the reading of the English dead. The writer was outraged at such an intrusion: was Henry supposed to have taken the organ to battle with him, he demanded. You don't think that your music might evoke a similar response?

Guy Woolfenden: Well, you certainly always get purists who complain that the music is out of period, and that sort of thing. Which I think is silly because Shakespeare belongs to every period, and every generation, and can't be confined in that way. But I think most people now accept the convention of music and plays, because of films. It never occurs to people now, I'm sure, when they see the Olivier film, with Walton's marvellous music, to wonder how Henry took a symphony orchestra to Agincourt. I would mind very much, though, if I went to see *Henry V*, and they used bits of Beethoven and Tchaikovsky. At least my humble contributions are specially written for each production, and not something Beethoven wrote for a completely different purpose.

Q: What about the one thing you mentioned earlier which *wasn't* specifically written for this production–the tape of the Agincourt battle?

Guy Woolfenden: Terry asked me if we could keep that, exactly as it was in the 1964 production. He didn't think that it could be bettered, and, in a sense, it was a sort of homage, a tip of the hat, to a production that we all admired. The tape is

used at that point in the play where you expect the battle
to begin, and where in fact Shakespeare does the amazing
thing of representing the whole of Agincourt by two
clowns–Pistol and Le Fer. It lasts for about forty seconds:
you hear the sounds of a cavalry charge, then the flight of
arrows, than a further cavalry charge, and then the sounds
of hand to hand fighting, the groans and the cries of injured
men. In fact what you hear isn't arrows, because you can't
record the sound of their flight properly–so that's done by
swishing canes, and by other electronic effects. It's in
quadrophonic sound–we've improved the sound quality a
little from what we were able to do in 1964–and it fills the
theatre. The stage is completely bare, except for the
Chorus–one man alone at the back of that huge stage. And
what I hope it does is give the audience an aural stimulus,
so that their visual imaginations begin to work, and they
begin actually to see the horror of that battle. It's just forty
seconds of assistance, so that, in the words of the Chorus,
they can 'mind true things, by what their mockeries be.'

THE ACTORS

ALAN HOWARD–HENRY V

Q: The last time you acted in a Shakespeare play, was as Theseus/Oberon in Peter Brook's production of *A Midsummer Night's Dream*. Did you feel there were any similarities between what was done to that play–the stripping away of all the theatrical traditions that had adhered to it–and what you were trying to do with *Henry V*?

Alan Howard: Yes I did. Brook and the cast tried to make the *Dream* more available than it has been in the past, perhaps, by a very direct and simple approach to the language of the play. And I hope that has happened also with *Henry V*: we are playing more of the text than is usual, and we approached the words very directly. Once you do that then I think the complexities and ambiguities of the play become apparent. People have tried to do *Henry V* as a play glorifying war, and a play condemning war; but by allowing the text to be free, without preconceptions, one discovers that the play does both those things and many others besides. A tradition of playing had been imposed on the *Dream*–cardboard forests and pretty fairies with gauze wings and so on: I think a similar tradition had grown up around *Henry V*: it tended to be seen as an extended pageant play, just as the *Dream* had been seen as a delightful fairy-story.

Q: You played Hal/Henry somewhat later in your career than many actors–after you had played parts such as Edgar in *Lear*, and Hamlet, rather than before. Do you think that affected your playing?

Alan Howard: It made an enormous difference, and I was very glad that I did play the parts that way round. There seemed to me to be some similarities in the themes of those plays and the '*Henries*'–the concern with being and seeming, with role playing–and the situations of the characters had a number of parallels. Hal, Edgar and Hamlet are all young men in a state of fierce indecision, and like them, Henry, in *Henry V*, has to go through a great number of tests, or gates, in order to come closer to what he really is. Henry faces many of the same issues that perplex Hamlet and Edgar–the problems of honour, justice, of whether people speak the truth, of loyalty, of action. And there are parallels in the relationships

52

within the plays – Edgar, his father and Lear; Hamlet, his father and Claudius; Hal, his father and Falstaff; in each case the younger man is having to deal with older men, with people in authority. When I first read *Henry V*, it struck me that Henry's situation was very much what Hamlet's might have been, if he had lived, and had had to fight Fortinbras. The interesting thing about *Henry V* is that it is the play in which the younger person goes on alone, without the presence of any of those older men.

Q: There is emphasis on the king's youth, isn't there, right at the beginning of *Henry V*?

Alan Howard: Yes there is, and it seems to me very important, a strong factor in the development of the play. Henry's very youth, and more important, his recent reformation, make him somewhat suspect. After his father's death, at the end of *Part Two*, when his brothers are clearly a little dubious about him, Henry goes out of his way to reassure them: 'This is the English, not the Turkish court./Not Amurath an Amurath succeeds,/But Harry, Harry.' And at the beginning of *Henry V*, when the Archbishop and Ely are discussing the change that has come over him, the Archbishop says, somewhat sardonically, 'It must be so, for miracles are ceased.' He seems to have certain doubts about Ely's comfortable explanation of Hal's reform. At the beginning of the play, Henry is very much an unknown quantity. No-one is quite sure which way he is going to jump.

Q: Although you opened in *Henry V* first, you rehearsed that play and *Henry IV Part One* in tandem, and, obviously, you knew you were going to play Hal/Henry right through three plays. Did you feel that the character of Hal linked with that of Henry?

Alan Howard: When we began rehearsals we worked on *Henry V* for one half of the day, and *Henry IV Part One* for the other half. And gradually one began to see that the whole question of acting, and assuming roles, which is so central to the early Hal, is also carried through into *Henry V*. Each of the three plays is very different, in structure and mood, but there is a clear line through them on Henry. In *Part One* he is externally very involved with others – the whole close society of the Boar's Head – but the seeds of isolation are there. By *Henry V*, he has become completely isolated, he is under an enormous magnifying glass, and has very few opportunities for normal human communications. The man who watches others in *Part One*—and who assumes roles and uses acting devices, like disguise in order to do so, has become the man that everyone is looking at, and looking to, for leadership and so on. It seemed to me that the Henry at the beginning of *Henry V* still cannot put off the masks that he was accustomed to using as Hal. It is only when the events become more and more dramatic, and he is forced into a corner, that the mask begins to slip—begins to fail him. If Hal were not so used to using masks, playing roles, then he would perhaps find it easier to be the straightforward warrior-king in *Henry V,* that so many commentators assume him to be. That, for me, was the most important link between Hal and Henry: there are numerous others.

Q: Right at the beginning of *Henry V* you come up against the problem that worries many people: Henry decides to go to war with France. What do you feel about that decision, and its subsequent implications through the play?

Alan Howard: It's worth examining the scene where that decision is reached fairly closely. There are at least five strong reasons for his going to France, though they are not necessarily what you might call 'moral' ones. First, on the purely practical side he has problems with the Church; in the previous play the rebellion against his father has been led by the Archbishop of York; this Archbishop is urging him to go to war, and promising him money to do so, as a way of avoiding conflict with Church interests. Second, I think he undoubtedly wants the return of his great-grandfather's lands in France. Third, he knows the problems disunity caused in his father's reign, and presumably he remembers his father's death-bed advice. 'Be it thy course to busy giddy minds/With foreign quarrels'. War with France then, might bring England peace and tranquility. Fourth, I think he is clearly obsessed with the nature of his own inheritance. In the night scene he begs God not to think about the fault his father made in compassing the crown, and at the end of *Henry IV Part Two* he is determined that, whatever the doubts about his inheritance, he will hand the crown on to his own son:

> And put the world's whole strength
> Into one giant arm, it shall not force

This lineal honour from me. This from thee
Will I to mine leave, as 'tis left to me.

Those are extraordinarily passionate words: a successful war with France is a way of assuring his hold on the crown. Fifth, everyone on the stage with him is reminding him of the feats of his ancestors. Those all seem to me to be very powerful motivations. Even so, he doesn't go straight off and do it, he's keeps raising problems: the slaughter that will result, the political problem of the Scots. It's only when there is a sixth factor, the insult of the Dauphin, that he finally blows, and makes the decision.

But the most important reason of all, I think, is that war is going to force him into further self-discovery. The king at war is the next role he has to take up. Going to France is the next test of himself, in terms of the long Odyssey of self-exploration that he began long ago in the earlier plays.

Q: The concept of Henry as a voyager is not one that has been widely shared by critics of the play. One commentator asserts for instance, that before the play begins 'it's central conflict has already been resolved. Henry's character is fully developed.' Many people seem to find him a static character.

Alan Howard: I can't understand that reaction. I think it's completely wrong. Just look at the structure of the play, it's extraordinary, a series of stops and starts right up to the battle of Agincourt, which is almost two thirds of the way through. If Shakespeare had wanted to show a man who was going to cut through this situation like a knife through butter, he could have done so. Why doesn't he? Almost all the way through you have a similar pattern: Off to France (after a lot of deliberation and prevarication)–no, pause: Falstaff is ill. Off to France again at Southampton–no, pause: the traitors. Off to France again at the end of that scene, 'Cheerly to sea, the signs of war advance–no, pause: Falstaff is dead. Further pause for the French, who are undecided how to act; the breach–the first sign of action, Henry gets some of his men over the breach, Nym Bardolph, Pistol and the Boy remain; and the four captains quarrel. Harfleur, and the violent speech to the Governor–then, immediately afterwards, when the city capitulates, the decision to withdraw, to retreat. That pattern goes on and on; even the decision to fight the French at Agincourt is made because of a foolishness of timing – the French decide to fight just as the English are about to slope off to Calais and go home. And if you look at those halts, those interruptions, you begin to see that each time they happen Henry is faced, either directly, or obliquely, with a decision. When I noticed that, I began to think that maybe what was going on here was an examination of the whole relationship between decision and action. Every time Henry attempts to solve a problem by action, the problems and the decisions compound. He has to cross a formidable number of hurdles and palpably, they change him. The very way he speaks is affected: look at the change from the public voice of the opening scenes, and the interior voice of the night scenes – 'I think the king is but a man, as I am: the violet smells to him as it doth to me'.

Q: But the play does have an extraordinary critical history, doesn't it? It's very hard to find a commentator, from Dr. Johnson to Yeats who doesn't find the play shallow or jingoistic. Why do you think that is?

Alan Howard: Well, they haven't had to play it. It seems to me a quite different experience, reading a play in the solitude of one's study, and actually performing it on the stage. It is a *play*, after all, not a novel. It's written for actors, for the spoken voice. I think what often happens is that people like the ones you quote can't hear a voice when they read the words. They see a line like 'None else of name', as Henry says after the reading of the English nobles' deaths, and they say, 'ah ha! a callous snob unaware of the realities of war for his ordinary soldiers'. It doesn't seem to occur to them that there are a dozen ways you could inflect those words to give them a different meaning. They seem to me sad and ironic, maybe even something written at the bottom of the scroll of names he's been reading. But perhaps you have to perform the play to that point to be aware of their ambiguity.

Q: Henry has often been seen as a kind of pious public-school hero – in fact that's one of the reasons so many critics dislike and dismiss the play. You obviously don't see him in those terms?

Alan Howard: There is an extraordinarily apt description of Hal in *Henry IV Part Two* which his father gives to Clarence:

> *He hath a tear for pity and a hand*
> *Open as day for meeting charity.*
> *Yet notwithstanding, being incensed, he's flint*

> *As humourous as winter…*
> *But being moody, give him Time and scope,*
> *Till that his passions, like a whale on ground,*
> *Confound themselves with working.*

He has hit on one of the key things in Henry's character, that he is a passionate man. We see that passion unleashed at Southampton on Scroop, and it's interesting that the very quality he praises in Scroop is his balance: 'Free from gross spirit, or of mirth or anger/Constant in spirit, not swerving with the blood'. There seems to be in Henry that constant tug between reason and passion that you find in all Shakespeare's great tragic heroes. It is reason that makes him put aside Falstaff, and reason that makes him allow Bardolph's execution. That he doesn't do that coldly, and without a struggle can be seen in the ramblings, the indecision, the contradictions of his speech to Montjoy immediately after Bardolph's death. He is so conscious of the force and power of passion that he performs it, acts it, because he knows that it can be a spur at a particular point in the action. 'Imitate the action of the tiger,' he says, as if by imitating wrath you can effect it. His speeches ring with an awareness of the horrors of passion unleashed: the first message to the Dauphin, the speech to the Governor of Harfleur. In that speech, war, the ultimate unleashing of passion, is linked closely to images of Hell:

> *What is it then to me, if impious war*
> *Array'd in flames, like to the prince of fiends,*
> *Do, with his smirch'd complexion, all fell feats*
> *Enlinked to waste and desolation?*

And in the midst of that particular conflict, what is his constant obsession? It is with truth, a truth that steers a course between both extremes, a rather simple truth—is someone a man of his word? He asks that in the earlier plays of Poins and Falstaff, both of whom disappoint him. And he asks it in this play of Scroop and of Williams. It is also asked of him, by Williams, who doubts the king's word about his ransom, and perhaps it is this question that triggers his searching examination of his own identity in the night scene.

Q: Do you mean in the ceremony speech?

Alan Howard: No, the whole scene. He begins the scene by, it seems to me, acting the cheerfulness he knows is required of him as a commander. Then he starts putting on disguises again, just as he did as Hal. He puts on Erpingham's cloak; he pretends to Pistol that he is Harry le Roy–'a Welshman'; he pretends to Williams that he is under Erpingham's command. What he is doing is precisely what he later accuses Bates of doing, of speaking this 'to feel other men's minds'. So his identity is confused again, by the adoption of masks–although the masks he chooses, a Welshman, a 'friend', are interesting, because they are quite close to the truth. Then Williams confronts him with the whole question of the king's responsibility for his soldiers in war. I think he answers Williams somewhat inadequately, except that he does say 'every subject's soul is his own', which is a sudden and extraordinary admission of personal responsibility, his first articulation of that idea. He says that he *embraces* Williams' challenge, not that he accepts it, or some other weaker term. And I think he means that: he welcomes all the implications of that challenge, including the fact that it is *his* own challenge, turned upon himself. Is he a man of his word, or will he take refuge in the protection of status, of kingship, when the chips are finally down?

The ceremony speech is an angry bitter speech. He blisters his way through it. In no way is it a calm reflective speech followed by a sweet prayer. It is a sicking-up of everything in him, he is caught in the cross-fire of his own imagination. He pulls down all the symbols that represent the conventional king with huge ferocity; then he lashes out at people physically less well off than himself: he works himself up to a point where both sides are equally damned. But I find the great question of the speech is about the impotence of temporal power, its inability to change or help anyone, its inability even to bring peace and tranquility to the holder. Immediately after that he resorts to God; 'Possess them not with fear,' he prays for his soldiers, as if praying that his soldiers should not be like him as he is at that moment, reduced by the previous scene and the advent of the next day, to turmoil and fear. He tries to bargain with God, cravenly, because he is in extremity, but even at the moment that he does so he knows the prayer is pointless: 'Though all I can do is nothing worth,/Since that my penitence comes after all,/Imploring pardon.' At that moment, when he is at his lowest ebb, he hears Gloucester's voice. 'I will go with thee', he says, and then miraculously, perhaps because every cell in that body has been stretched and stressed and pulverised, he hits on a simple truth, 'The day, my friends, and all things stay for me.' It is the realisation that *his* soul is his own every bit as much as Williams'; the realisation that he must stop acting, stop hiding. When he says 'all things stay for me', I think he is saying much more than that his army is waiting for its leader. He is saying that events are waiting upon his ability to become himself. And at the end of that long night, he carries that new resolution within himself, into the morning, and into the battle.

Q: So do the masks drop after the night scene?

Alan Howard: Not exactly. When he makes the Crispin's Day speech the next morning it isn't just a performance any longer. The real man merges with the role, and makes it his own. He can talk freely and openly with his men. It is a revelation for him and for them. We know he has to save his army from obliteration, and he does it, but not with the kind of rhetoric he used at the breach. Perhaps they sense his new personal resolution. Perhaps he conveys to them a sense of each individual's reliance on, and interdependance with the others. Certainly they go into battle as a group of individuals united to one cause, and that makes them invincible.

Q: But after the battle, Henry assigns the victory to God, not brotherhood.

Alan Howard: Yes he does. But that has nothing to do with all the usual mouthings about his piety. I think he is genuinely aware that there has been a force in the battle that he–that no-one–can explain or analyse. And he is awed by that. When he says 'O God, thy arm *was* here' it is like a sudden discovery of God. It's in marked contrast to his attitude to God earlier in the play which ranges from the cursory 'For we have now no thought in us but France./Save those to God, which run before our business' to the rude 'Which God so graciously hath brought to light', he says, not sounding as if he means it, after the discovery of the traitors' plot at Southampton.

Before Agincourt his attitude to God is directly challenging: 'As thou pleasest God, dispose the day,' he says. At that point, he seems to be relying on the interior strength of his men–'All things are ready if our minds be so'. He makes no attempt before the battle to allege that God will fight on their side, as his father does before Shrewsbury. It's interesting that it is only in victory that he shows any real reverence.

Q: Do you think he glories in that victory?

Alan Howard: Not in the least. He asks simply that the dead with charity be 'enclos'd in clay'. He specifically forbids boasting of the victory. I don't think there is a single instance in the three plays where he glories in war, or glories over the death of his opponents. Look at his behaviour after Hotspur's death; he pays him complex, ritualistic respects, and when Falstaff chooses to pretend that he is responsible for the killing, he says, 'For my part, if a lie may do thee grace/I'll gild it with the happiest terms I have.' I think his compassion and honouring of those who have died in battle could not be more marked. He and Williams seem to me to share a vision of the horror and pity of war.

Q: After the war, comes wooing. And again, many critics of the play take exception to the last scene. Do you think it is tacked on, or integral to the rest?

Alan Howard: Absolutely integral. Isn't marriage the final stage of his particular Odyssey? I think by that point in the play Shakespeare has shown us a man who has been through all sorts of physical, moral and emotional tests; he has almost arrived at his completion. Where should he go next but into a true marriage of love and alliance with another human being? It is the wooing scene that determines his future, which is one of marriage and birth. He is to become the husband, and ultimately, the father.

Q: But isn't his wooing of Katherine somewhat crude and cursory? Isn't it, in any case, a political marriage?

Alan Howard: I don't think so. I think it is the resolution of the whole play. The match may begin as a political one, but during the course of the scene it becomes much more than that. Katherine is French: she does not speak his language, nor he hers. The scene is the final exploration of the theme which runs through all three plays of the inability of people to comprehend each other. Shakespeare uses language problems to illustrate the barriers people put between each other. Henry and Katherine break down those barriers; when he kisses her he says that her touch has more *eloquence* than any number of speeches. Katherine is a considerable woman: he does not woo her easily, and he does not offer her easy terms. He very carefully says that he will not be all the things that conventionally a woman might want a man to be: he will not be an elegant courtly lover; he will not be a gallant knight; he will not try a rough physical approach–though he could do or be all those things. But he consciously rejects the roles open to him, 'Thou hast me,' he tells her, 'if thou hast me, at the worst: and thou shalt wear me, if thou wear me, better and better'.

Q: Do you think finally, after playing Henry V for as long as you have done, that the play really is about war at all?

Alan Howard: I think it is a play about conflict; the conflict between men and their consciences; men and their fears; men's passion and their reason; the conflict between what is said and what is meant. The men in this play are at war, both with each other and within themselves. The war is a real activity, but it is also a metaphor.

EMRYS JAMES–CHORUS & BURGUNDY

Emrys James: It was always one of my ambitions to play the Chorus. I've wanted to play it ever since I left university, ever since I first decided to go into the theatre, I've wanted to play that part. And now I've done–what–116 performances of it, something like that, and I haven't begun to tire of it. You know how actors have favourite speeches, speeches that they do at auditions? Well, for years, I used to do 'O for a Muse of fire' as my audition speech. And then maybe I would get the part and maybe I wouldn't, but that speech, and the other Chorus speeches stayed with me in my head. I'd be walking down Oxford Street and there would be those extraordinary words, ticking over in my head, just there, for no reason at all, except that they'd been planted in my brain, and I'd go over and over them. And then, when I came to play the part finally I discovered something very odd, which was that I had remembered some speeches quite wrongly. I'd believed them to be one thing for years, and I was wrong. I'd always thought, for instance, that one of the lines – before the night scene – was 'The country cocks do crow, the bells do toll…' and in fact it's 'The clocks do toll…', which, when you think about it, is a much more remarkable image, all those little villages all over France, and their church clocks marking the passing of the night…So re-learning the speeches, which I had always loved, was a process of rediscovery all the time.

Q: For a long time when this play was produced in the eighteenth and early nineteenth centuries, they used either to cut the Chorus completely, or adapt it radically. Did it ever worry you that the Chorus might not be an integral part of the play – what did you see your function as Chorus being within the production?

Emrys James: No, it never occurred to me that you could separate the Chorus from the play. I think he is absolutely integral, and he fulfils a very particular function. You're very much on your own, of course; in a way it's a very lonely part – you're separated to an extent from the rest of the action. It seems to me that the main relationship the Chorus has, is with the audience. You are their guide; it's the duty of the Chorus to lure the audience into the play, to be friendly, to relax them, so their imaginations can start working on the scene that they're about to see. It's very obvious in the text that that is what he is doing – he keeps emphasizing it, 'Work, work your thoughts' – but in order to be able to do it, you have to win the audience's confidence, you have to establish a relationship with them from the first. Then when you ask them to start making those imaginative leaps, they want to do it. They're encouraged, not coerced.

Q: In this production, of course, the Chorus is further separated from the other actors by his costume – he remains in modern dress throughout. How did that 'loneliness' or separation as you describe it, affect you?

Emrys James: Well, it makes you rather vulnerable. If you make any kind of mistake there's no-one else playing with you to help you retrieve yourself. At one performance, for instance, I got to the line – 'Still be kind/And eke out our performance with your mind' which is the cue, in this production, for the raising of the breach. I looked round over my shoulder, and the ramp hadn't come up. I fled into the wings, and I was convinced I'd made a mistake. I was saying My god, my god, I've said the wrong speech, I've got them in the wrong order. In fact the lift mechanism hadn't worked. But instinctively I blamed myself.

Q: You feel then that the Chorus has a closer relationship with the audience than he does with the other actors?

Emrys James: Yes, I think so. It seems to me that the Chorus is given so many chances to build up a relationship with them. He makes little jokes–'And thence to France shall we convey you safe', he says, and then adds, 'And bring you back again'. He reassures, teases them. And he's very disarming, very modest. He admits all the limitations of the play and the production from the start; when the audience has just come in, and hasn't yet settled, he acknowledges the 'unworthy scaffold' that they're looking at, 'the wooden O'. He even asks their pardon for the insufficiency of the stage and the actors–and because he does that, I think audiences *are* won over, *are* lured into the play, do perhaps stop worrying about being in a theatre, and do begin to start using their imagination.

Q: What about the intense patriotic tone of some of the Chorus speeches? Some commentators have found his praise of Henry and the English rather over-stated. Doesn't it unbalance the play, and weight it in favour of the English?

Emrys James: I don't think he is partisan about the English. He says very aptly what the situation is–'the poor contemned English', which is what they are at that point. When he says that the French are 'Proud of their numbers' he is reporting fairly accurately what sort of state the French are in. He's not praising the English exactly.

Q: 'This star of England...'?

Emrys James: Well, maybe. But the Chorus doesn't set the French up to be knocked down. I think he reports fairly exactly on the state of each side. I suppose the speeches are patriotic. I don't quite know why one should be defensive about that. I suppose everybody derides patriotism nowadays, and I'm certainly not the sort of person who goes around waving a flag. But I know, all the same, that I can't listen to those speeches without being stirred. When you have lines like 'O England! model to thy inward greatness/Like little body with a mighty heart' it does seem to be something which sums up this country–we are small, we have shown greatness as a country in the past...I don't know. I've been through the stage of saying 'Rupert Brooke is rubbish', 'patriotism is the last refuge of a scoundrel', all that sort of thing. But still, there is something in those speeches which strikes a nerve, a response, and one can't ignore it or pretend it isn't there.

Q: The Chorus, in any case, is the person who qualifies all that, isn't he, in the very last speech of the play?

Emrys James: The last speech is extraordinary. I feel such admiration that a writer could do that: the strokes of his genius fall unerringly. After all that play about pride and honour and patriotism and war, he doesn't shirk the counterpoint to that for one second. There are the two people being talked about–Henry and Katherine–still on the stage, and Shakespeare says: yes, they married, and yes, they had a son, and you think everything is going to be happy and tranquil ever after. He builds right up to a climax–'Henry the Sixth, in infant bands crowned King'–and then he tells the truth. 'Whose state so many had the managing'–and already we're slipping, we've come down from kings to managers. And then you have it–'That they lost France, and made our England bleed'. Everything that has been built up in the play dies with that one line.

And then Shakespeare says–'Which oft our stage hath shown'–which is a line full of ambiguity: does he mean, well yes folks, we've done a lot of plays about that, or does he also mean that we–the actors and the playwrites–have tried to show you that kind of truth many times before, just as we do in this play?

Finally, the very last lines of the play are–'And, for their sake/In your fair minds, let this acceptance take'. Who is the 'their' he is talking about? Is it the characters in the play, the characters in history, the actors, the writers, or the dead; the dead of Agincourt, or the dead of any war? Or is it perhaps all of those people?

Q: Has playing the Chorus at last, and having to come to terms with speeches such at that one changed your view of the play?

Emrys James: Yes, it has, enormously. Until now I'd never been in it, although I'd seen it several times. And I suppose I took the general line on the play–that it's a good boisterous patriotic piece of work, with some marvellous poetry in it. Of course one is foolish ever to make an assumption like that about any play of Shakespeare's. The more you dig the more riches you find. I had never really noticed the sadnesses in the play, like the death of Bardolph, or that last Chorus speech. It is full of moments which are utterly uncompromising: you see people having choices, making decisions, and acting, and you see the full result of their actions, which is often very harsh, and ugly, Shakespeare doesn't dodge those moments at all.

Q: What about the emphasis throughout the play that what we are watching is a theatrical performance?

Emrys James: Well, the Chorus speeches are filled with a consciousness of theatre. The Chorus even sends actors up a little bit–'Prologue-like', he says, mocking that whole convention. All through the play I'm aware of the presence of the stage–the 'wooden O'–The stage itself becomes a palpable force in the play. I stand in the backdock sometimes and watch the actors scurrying about, the dressers rushing back and forth, and all that backstage activity seems somehow a part of the performance we're giving out front. You know that it must always have been much the same in any theatre, from the mediaeval mummers on, and that it always will be the same. And that kind of continuity, of action and acting, is very much what the play is about.

OLIVER FORD-DAVIES–MONTJOY; THE FRENCH AMBASSADOR, THE GOVERNOR OF HARFLEUR.

Q: Can we begin by talking about Montjoy? Montjoy, as he is in this production, differs considerably from the Montjoy in Shakespeare's play. He has assimilated the parts of several other French nobles, and become a much fuller and more considerable force in the play. How did that happen, and did the changing of the text worry you?

Oliver Ford-Davies: Normally I find I'm very rigid about sticking exactly to what Shakespeare wrote. You know, often in a rehearsal, or even in performance, an actor will change the text–he'll stick in a word or phrase of his own intentionally, or he will learn something wrongly and never correct it. That always irritates me immensely. I think you should play what Shakespeare wrote. But with this play, I found I didn't mind these changes, I approved them. They seemed to me to give greater strength to the French area of the play, and to tie up some of the knots that had been left unravelled. The whole development of Montjoy was a gradual, continuous process. I didn't come to rehearsals with all my speeches marked out for me. Quite the reverse. I found in the early days of rehearsal that I was being called for scenes that I didn't appear to be in, and that gradually I would take a line, or be given a line, in one of those scenes, and so the character built up, but very slowly, very gradually. There are so many characters in Shakespeare who are given only twenty lines, but who seem to have a whole wealth of experiences, a whole life, suggested by those lines–and then they disappear, they're cut off in their prime. Shakespeare seems to have a great interest in Montjoy, but in the play as it stands that isn't fully developed. Instead he introduces other characters, like Grandpré and Rambures, who say a few lines, never develop and then disappear. We cut them, and expanded Montjoy with all the lines that were freed, and we built a man who is the one major intermediary between the French and the English. And as we did so, a discernable character began to emerge. There were lines that seemed right for him, and other lines which obviously weren't. I don't know how much Terry had decided and pre-determined what those lines were, but they were certainly discussed, and changed considerably in rehearsal. And when I began to relax and play the play it felt right. There was a man there who made sense to me.

Q: What sort of a man was that?

Oliver Ford-Davies: Well, I think we began from a concept of the two courts. Terry saw the English court as informal, first seen in ordinary actors' rehearsal clothes etc. And the French court as the opposite to that–mediaeval, archaic and chivalric. But the French were, all the same, a force to be reckoned with: the French king was strong, not senile as he is often played, and the Dauphin was a sort of mirror image of Hal–a prince chafing against his father's restraints, impulsive, longing for war, immature perhaps, but formidable. And it was very important that the other people in that court should be as distinct and individual as their counterparts in the English court. Montjoy is the only representative of the French court who meets the English–he relays all the information about them, he is the only man who, until the end of the play has the chance of encountering a different kind of king, and a different kind of court–so he becomes a character of enormous importance. The French have a kind of insular quality–he ventures outside that. Then, as I began to read through the speeches and the play again, it seemed to me that the key to Montjoy lay in his encounters with Henry. He meets him three times, twice before Agincourt, and once after the battle. These meetings reveal certain things about him, and they also reveal that he changes–he isn't a static personality at all. He seems to me to have a certain strength, a certain intelligence, (which Henry recognises by taking a particular interest in him, asking his name and so on) and he also has a certain liberality of outlook. His mind is not closed, he is influenced by what he sees of Henry and the English army.

Q: Those three encounters with Henry are all there in the original text. How did they affect your shaping of Montjoy in the French scenes, where the text is substantially re-ordered and re-allocated?

Oliver Ford-Davies: I think Montjoy starts off very much as a conventional member of the French court. He shares to a degree their arrogance and self-assurance. I saw him as a sort of Burke Trend figure–the PPS on the sidelines, taking notes on discussions, as I do in the first French scene, and also in the night scene. But he is also something of a diplomat, a peace maker. It seemed right for him to try and intervene between the other French noblemen in the night scene, when they are all quarrelling, and to make a remark like the one he makes about the Constable's armour, because he is trying to find a neutral topic, something to calm the irritation that exists between the others. But he develops from there: because he is the only person who has actually encountered the English, it seemed right that before Agincourt it should be he who sees the English army as something more than a pathetic ragged band who will be decimated in the coming battle–so

he has the speech–'The horsemen sit like fixed candlesticks…'
It isn't a triumphant speech, a rejoicing in the malaise of
the English army–it's a worried considered speech–he's
saying, yes, they *are* ragged and pathetic, but isn't that
extraordinary, and perhaps, in its way, impressive? The speech
subdues the others, and it seemed exactly right that Montjoy,
who has some knowledge of this army, should say it.

Q: But you say that you think Montjoy develops as a character, and that
he is changed by his encounters with Henry and the English. In what way?
Oliver Ford-Davies: The first time Montjoy encounters Henry
dressed exactly like his soldiers–there is no indication that he is
the King. And the English army are at, perhaps, their lowest
ebb. The second time he encounters him is immediately after
the Crispin's Day speech, when Montjoy comes for a second
time to bid Henry consider of his ransom. He makes his
speech, and there is a rather odd sequence immediately after
it. Henry says to him, 'Who hath sent thee now?', which,
if you consider it, is a peculiar question. And Montjoy says,
'The Constable.' At the same rehearsal, and quite
independantly Alan and I discovered the possibility that
Montjoy might be lying at that point. We don't telegraph
it particularly, it's just there to be picked up, but it's a turning
point, for me, in Montjoy. I feel certain that when he makes
the second visit to Henry, before the battle, he has gone there
on his own authority, he's gone there to try and stop the
battle. Henry senses that, and that is why he asks him who
has sent him. What happened next in our production was
that Montjoy was made to witness the extraordinary unity
of the English army. And at that point I tore up my badge
of office, the leafy branch that I had entered with. I think,
faced with what he sees of the English army, Montjoy realises
that his whole function, his whole world has become archaic.
He cannot function any longer as a mediaeval herald.

Q: What about the actual battle of Agincourt itself? In this production
Montjoy is constantly present, and becomes, finally, the sole representative
of the French–he is very much Henry's opposite number.
Oliver Ford-Davies: Gradually in rehearsal Montjoy was
introduced into those scenes more and more. He witnesses
the death of the boy, for instance, and I think is horrified
by it. And it is Montjoy that actually announces that the

battle is over, it is he who says, 'The day is yours'. That is as it is in the original text, of course, but I think that perhaps the way we do it is a departure from tradition. I believe that it is often done very formally–Montjoy hands over a staff of office, or something of that sort. In rehearsal I was doing it half formally, half passionately, and Terry said, 'Go on, go on, do it as you feel it.' and I realised suddenly that this was right. At this point, I think Montjoy passionately wants an end to all this carnage. He is almost shell-shocked, he is stunned by the horror of what he has seen on the battlefield. And he is a non-combatant, almost a reporter figure–I thought of a sort of James Cameron–he is partisan, of course, but he does not fight, heralds never did, and so he is impotent. All he can do is acknowledge a victory so that the slaughter can end.

Q: At the very end of the battle, when the reading of the dead is over, and the English soldiers leave, with a kind of supressed jubilation, Montjoy and Henry are left behind. They leave the field of battle alone, and together, and pause together and look back. The victory becomes a very sobering, not a glorious thing. Why did you do that?

Oliver Ford-Davies: That whole moment has changed a good deal during the performances we've given. I still don't know what audiences pick up from it, and I've never really discussed it with Alan, perhaps because I thought it was better left unspoken between us: I felt it was working, and I didn't want us to talk it into the ground, to over-investigate it. For me, it seems to say, look, we both know that there is no victor in warfare, that, after such carnage concepts like winning seem irrelevant. I suppose that's a twentieth century idea, and one has to be wary of it as such–in the fifteenth century victory did mean something very tangible. But I still feel that after what has happened Henry and Montjoy share a complexity and doubt about this slaughter. I think that, after Henry says, 'God fought for us', Montjoy is filled with doubts about the French, about his world, and about why God was not on their side. And over and above that, I think he is sickened, as Henry is, by what he has just witnessed on the battlefield. The French have been trapped in their armour, and their armour, which was supposed to protect them, has become the instrument of their death. And that is a curiously twentieth century image–like men trapped in tanks, or nuclear bomb shelters. He has just seen his army dying inside the devices designed to protect it, the glorious devices they all boasted about the night before the battle. And I think he is appalled by it. He shares that moment with Henry, and no-one else.

Q: You say that Montjoy progresses from being the conventional, Frenchman, sharing all the French concepts of hierarchy, to something else, after he witnesses the different kind of army Henry creates among the English. Yet Montjoy's first reaction after the battle is to plead that the French be allowed to go about the battlefield, and 'sort our nobles from our common men'. He seems appalled that French princes should be lying soaked in what he calls 'mercenary blood'. How do you equate such a reaction at such a moment with the change in the man that you've described?

Oliver Ford-Davies: That speech brings one up against a problem. It makes me question, certainly, how much I'm playing Shakespeare's Montjoy and how much a newly created character. You could argue away the problem by saying, 'well, Montjoy cannot grow up overnight'. I don't know. Perhaps it's the point where our break from Shakespeare shows. But in performance I find it can co-exist with the man, and with the changes that have happened to him. It's a strongly emotional speech. It's the words of a man who has just witnessed an appalling battle. The transition, the co-existence of the two attitudes, seems possible.

Q: You've said that you think Montjoy's encounters with Henry change him. Does Shakespeare make this a one-way process do you think, or is it more than that?

Oliver Ford-Davies: I think it is clearly a two-way thing. Henry is not a static character, any more than Montjoy is. I think that Shakespeare certainly shows us that Henry is also affected by those meetings. Montjoy represents every thing that Henry is in conflict with–and yet Shakespeare clearly intends him to find Montjoy a sympathetic person. It's an over simplification to say that the new renaissance man meets the mediaeval archaic man, because Henry is not the new renaissance man, yet–he's in the process of discovering what that might be. But the meetings with Montjoy seem to me to force Henry towards self-realization, perhaps even towards an understanding of the need for unity in his army and his country. It is when Montjoy appears that Henry is forced to be aware of the disunity among the English. And it is after they meet for the second time, that the army is most at one with Henry. I think Montjoy is the catalyst for that.

Q: Besides Montjoy you also play the Ambassador to Henry's court at the beginning of the play, and the Governor of Harfleur. Why use the same actor?

Oliver Ford-Davies: Again, I think we wanted to make the point that there is a difference between the French who have encountered Henry, and those who have not. So all the French who do meet Henry are played by the same person. It isn't stated visually, because I look different as the Ambassador, and as the Governor I speak from the back of the auditorium, and I'm not seen. But it is the same voice, and perhaps people register that. It seems to me right because all the French who do meet Henry appear to share the same attitude of respect for him–'Question your grace the late ambassadors,/With what great state he heard their embassy', the Constable says. So much of the play seems to deal with the difficulties of communication between people, which is compounded, in the case of the French and the English, by the fact that the vital people on each side have never even *met* each other. I think it's very significant at the end of the play that the king of France says to Henry 'Right joyous are we to behold thy *face*'. The two sides are meeting, really meeting, without intermediaries, for the first time.

TREVOR PEACOCK–FLUELLEN, THE WELSH CAPTAIN.

Q: How did you start working on the character of Fluellen?

Trevor Peacock: Well, I think the most important thing about Fluellen is his Welshness. He's not just *a* Welshman in this play, he is *the* Welshman. I'd never played a Welshman before, so the first thing I concentrated on was the accent. When you go on a stage you know that you've got to become the person you're playing. You have to move like them and speak like them. Now no-one in the audience was going to notice much if I didn't move like a Welshman–but if I didn't talk like one–well, forget it. So I drilled myself. I went to see an old friend of mine who is not only Welsh–he's very Welsh, in the sense that he loves words and beer and rugby–and I arrived on his doorstep one night, and said, 'Would you very much mind reading the whole part for me and I'll tape it.' 'Lovely, boy,' he said, 'no problems', and he did it–though in fact he started to freeze up a bit, and felt he had to give it all an interpretation–but anyway, he did it, and I took it away and played it and played it and played it. And I listened to records of *Under Milk Wood*, and Dylan Thomas's poetry, and after a bit I began to believe that I'd make a reasonable stab at it. Then I did what I always do, with any part I'm playing, I taped it myself, but several versions, all in different moods, one very quiet perhaps, and another very angry, until I knew all the words backwards. I have to do all that, because otherwise, when I go into rehearsal I have no idea about the character, I don't know where he belongs. I can't just read plays, you see, not ones I'm going to be in, anyway. They don't exist for me in print, I'm like a child of six or seven reading them. They only really start to exist for me when the people who are going to do it get together.

Then, when we'd been rehearsing for a while, I made another tape of the scenes I was in, but reading all the other characters' lines, and leaving gaps for Fluellen's bits. Then I can time roughly how long I've got for my speeches, and what sort of pace the scene is going at. Finally I make one last tape of the whole thing, mimicking the others, because by then they're beginning to settle into a way of doing a speech. I have to do all that, I'm a mixture of total confidence and total lack of confidence, and I can't go on unless I'm 100% confident.

After that it's a question of growing into the part and the play as you rehearse it. I find that there's only about six moments in all the rehearsal time when, whoosh, suddenly it comes to you, and everything starts to go in the right direction. And those moments come to all the actors on quite different days–but they always do come, sooner or later. And then you find what to give, and how.

Q: Did you ever try, consciously, to make Fluellen funny?

Trevor Peacock: No, never. If you try to be funny you're finished. I knew that if I made Fluellen real then he would be funny, because many of the lines are funny. But it's no good thinking of them as gags, or separate from the character of the man that says them. I'm a small man, and so naturally, I thought of Fluellen in terms of his being small. Small men are funnier than big men, I think, because they've grown up being little, and they have to push harder. There's an extrovert inside the introvert, the scholar, in Fluellen, and it's always suddenly bursting out. That's one of the things that perhaps makes him funny. He is very full of contradictions: he's a stickler for the rules, and obsessed with law and order and organisation and the Roman wars, but he's also a wild romantic, a sentimentalist, and a hero-worshipper. He starts off by singing the praises of the Duke of Exeter, but as soon as a bigger star – the king – appears on the horizon, he forgets about the duke altogether. And because of all those things he's very easily moved – I'm sure that when he's listened to the king delivering the Crispin's Day speech, he would be weeping tears into the dawn. I don't do that, because it might be a bit distracting on stage – but I'm sure he would.

Q: There are unpleasant sides to Fluellen's character I think – his harshness and selfrighteousness regarding Bardolph and Williams, for instance. Did you feel that?

Trevor Peacock: Yes – but I think you see that side to him most strongly in the scene between the four captains, at Harfleur. You've got to remember that Henry comes on immediately after that scene, addresses the Governor, and warns him about the rape and pillage and plunder that is going to result if he unleashes his army. The four captains, including Fluellen, are part of that army, and I think you've got to believe that those men are capable of doing those kinds of things. They are ruthless and brutal – and you must see that ruthlessness and brutality in the scene between them. It isn't a cosy jokey little scene about a Welshman, Scotsman, Englishman and Irishman.

Q: In this production the English army consists of thirteen men, including the king, so you and the other captains are very noticeably a part of that army. There are long stretches when you're on stage, but have nothing to say. How did you rehearse these sequences?

Trevor Peacock: We did a lot of improvisation. We had a great heap of towels and tents and cooking utensils in the rehearsal rooms, and everyday we built a camp, and kitted ourselves up from it, and after a bit it began to work – one got the feel of a soldier, of being part of an army. And we rehearsed the breach sequence, for instance, like rugby–we didn't have a wall to push against, so we formed a scrum, and pushed against each other. People got really violent–and then Terry would yell 'Break', and we'd break, and go into the scene. And we'd all be panting and sweaty and angry and steaming with heat–flat out, practically finished, so it really took something big in the next speech to get us back over that wall. That scene used to be really good when we did that: it's falling off a bit now. Half the time, people come over that ramp and they look as if they've come straight out of a scented bath. But that's one of the penalties of a long-running show. You have to fight that kind of falling-off all the time.

Q: Have you ever served in the forces yourself?

Trevor Peacock: Did National Service, in the Army. I spent most of my time running the garrison theatre. But I suppose I was trained–I did route marching, bayonet charging–enough to understand a little bit why the armies that win are the ones where the soldiers have lost their individuality. It's a funny thing–that ability of men to become part of a fighting group–there seems to be something in it that appeals to every man, a kind of 2000 year old inherited memory. And that's what happens in this play–that army does get welded together. I don't know whether I approve of that, or think it means very much–I don't know. When I was trained to fight it was never put to the test. Now I don't believe in wars or in fighting–but the thing does happen, that unification, for good or bad, and I think you see it in *Henry V* very clearly.

Q: If you feel dubious about the worth of that kind of army unity, army comradeship, how do you feel about the play, do you admire it?

Trevor Peacock: I'm not sure. I used to think it was a rather boring pageant with some delightful speeches. Now I'm not sure. It has to be so well done. I don't think I'd put it in my Shakespeare Top Ten.

Q: Terry Hands thinks it's one of his five greatest plays.

Trevor Peacock: Oh God, that's because he's just done it. Directors always think the play they've just done is *the* masterpiece. Maybe it's that I don't say enough. That and the fact that there's no time for Scrabble in the second half. Ego, you see. I like fat parts.

Q: Fluellen's a fat part.

Trevor Peacock: Not fat enough! He could do with some more scenes.

PETER BOURKE–THE BOY

Q: As well as playing the Boy in *Henry V*, you also play Francis in the previous plays. Does that alter the part for you somewhat?

Peter Bourke: Very much. It means that, as a character, the Boy has seen the man who is now his king in quite a different context, that of the Boar's Head. He's observed the king in that other life he led, so he has a semi-relationship with the king, although he is now very distant from him. I used that fact at certain points in the play. If you're playing the trilogy, it does seem to make sense for the Boy to be played by Francis–it's really either him, or Falstaff's page, and the fact that Francis is the one associated with the Boar's Head, and the Boy with those characters in *Henry V* does give a strong link. And he has the line, after the breach scene, when he wishes he were in an ale-house in London.

Q: What do you think his role is in the action of *Henry V*?

Peter Bourke: When people talk about the part, they all say, 'Oh what a marvellous part, you have that terrific speech, and so on', but I think the boy is much more than someone who comes on with two good speeches to the audience. He's very real, very closely drawn. He seems to have two courses open to him, at the start of the play, will he become a thief as Bardolph and Pistol and Nym want him to be–in other words, will he become like them? or will he break from that, and try to be something else? So he is distanced from them, and I suppose helps to distance the audience from them by what he says about them, but he also seems to be very loyal, and very affectionate. He is the one who first comes in with the news of Falstaff's worsening illness, and tries to bring the old friends to him. And he shows a lot of affection for Pistol and Bardolph and Nym. They are the only three people that he has any contact with directly once they go to war, but although he knows they are rogues, he's not bitchy or snide about them, he doesn't ridicule them. I think he has

H.V.—F

love for them, but not respect, which is an important distinction in the context of the rest of the play.

Q: He's the youngest person on stage isn't he?

Peter Bourke: Yes, and I think he is a character of sympathy for the audience. It's not exactly that he is every mother's son, but there is something of that in it. He has an enormous innocence, but he's not in any way wet. He is without cruelty, and he is vulnerable. And of course, he gets killed.

Q: He is present, onstage, in this production more than he might be in others, isn't he, because he always comes on with the rest of the army?

Peter Bourke: He is with the luggage cart, which is where he is finally killed, all through the production. And from knowing that, in rehearsals other things emerged. The Boy is the one who is in charge of all the luggage on the cart, and so he is also the one who gives out food and drink to Henry and the Army. In the scene at the bridge, for instance, when we worked on it, I wondered what the Boy would be doing at that point, and I decided that he was giving drinks to the wounded. So that when Henry came on I gave him a drink also, and it happened that the moment I did that was the moment when Henry was about to give the final order for Bardolph's death. And so it seemed right that the Boy would do something, that he would plead for him. And so I go down on my knees to Henry at that point. That all came about from the kinds of questions that Terry asked each of us in rehearsal, when he asked us individually what we were doing in scenes, what our reactions were to what was going on. At first I used to plead from much further back, upstage, but Terry suggested that because I knew Henry from the Boar's Head days, I would perhaps go right down to him. Which I did. Immediately afterwards I run off the stage, because I think the Boy's first thought at that point would be to go to Bardolph, even if it was only to help bury his body. I don't know how much audiences even notice the details of that–like the fact that I come back on with the mug that Bardolph always carried–it's not that it should be that big anyway, but it is there, a through-line from the previous plays. I hope that it contributes a little to the moment, that it points up the weight of the king's decision, that perhaps it even makes it a little more difficult for him to make it: because after all, what he is doing at that point is executing Bardolph for something very similar to what he did himself on Gadshill all those years before, and Bardolph is his *friend*. The Boy is a reminder at that point of the weight of those old friendships and those old loyalties, which the Boy, although he criticises the Bardolph group, still hasn't broken from.

Q: What about the scene before the Battle of Agincourt, and the way you wake up the English army?

Peter Bourke: Again that came gradually, in rehearsal. Terry had told us all to find our places on the stage for the night scene, how and where we would choose to sleep and so on. And obviously the Boy would sleep by the cart, so that when we had to wake up in the morning for the battle, I was surrounded by all the luggage, all the pots and pans. Terry said to us one day, 'OK, you're all asleep, and when I say start, I want you to begin the day, wake up for that battle.' And when he did say start, I banged one of the pots on the cart, just as the kind of signal you might have in an army, that the day was starting, and there was food, or drink to be had. It comes, of course, immediately after, and contrasts with, the music and excitement of the exit of the French. And then it happened that all through the early part of the Crispin's Day speech, I was giving the army a drink – whatever it is, mugs of something, gruel perhaps. And that Alan then came up to me at a certain point of the speech, by which time everyone had drinks except me, and I had just poured my own. So I gave him the mug I would have used, when he came up to me. It's an ordinary wooden mug, not one of the jewelled ones, that he has been drinking from in all the Boar's Head scenes, and the previous scenes in *Henry V*.

Q: When the Boy *is* finally killed later in the play, it happens very quickly and suddenly. Why did you do it like that?

Peter Bourke: It seems so ironic that the Boy is killed immediately after the scene with Pistol and Le Fer, when it seems to me that he is very anxious, in his position as interpreter, to stop Pistol from cutting the Frenchman's throat. And as we arrange the scene order, he is also killed immediately after his own speech in which he says that the luggage, and the boys guarding it, would be easy prey for the French. When we first did it, I thought that those words might almost be a premonition of his death, but that seemed wrong. It made the scene surreal rather than real. It seemed better that there should just be a moment of fear, and then, bang, his own throat has been cut, he's dead. It's the suddenness of war.

Q: A lot of people who've seen the production remember the Boy's 'bloodstained body', and the force of that image through the succeeding scenes.

Peter Bourke: Do they really? That's very good in a way if they do, because there isn't any blood, we're not using it. The Boy's body is there, and it seems to be a force, an actual instance of the ugliness of war, both for the Dauphin, and for Henry. But there's no blood. If they see it, then that's the power and force of the audience's imagination. All I have is some food, tucked away on my body. And Fluellen and Gower take it, later on, and eat it. Because that's the way war seems to be; they're soldiers, and they're practical, and they know the Boy has no further use for it.

THE FRENCH:

CLEMENT McCALLIN–THE FRENCH KING;
GEOFFREY HUTCHINGS–THE DAUPHIN;
BERNARD BROWN–THE CONSTABLE OF FRANCE.

Q: I know that Terry Hands had a certain conception of the French king and his court before he began work on the play. Did you feel that that conception was imposed on you, or did you reach it yourselves through your characters and through rehearsal?

Clement McCallin: I think it evolved through rehearsal. And through character. When we first went into rehearsal, I remember saying to Terry that I thought the French king should be played strong. Traditionally, it seems to me, he's been played very much as the historical character was–senile, weak, mad. The text didn't seem to me to bear that out at all. He's a very forceful man–just look at his speech summoning up the French nobility to battle–and he is a true adversary of Henry: he isn't someone who is just going to be trampled over. And Terry agreed with that.

Geoffrey Hutchings: Through character. So often the French have just been portrayed as being thoroughly decadent, and the Dauphin is usually very effete, very camp. People seem to get him confused with Shaw's Dauphin, or maybe that influences their thinking, I don't know. But he didn't seem to me like that. For me, the key line of the Dauphin's is 'I desire nothing but odds with England.' I don't see the man who makes that kind of statement can be feeble and effeminate. He may be something of a hot-head, but he is a force to be reckoned with.

Bernard Brown: Well, we were helped in that approach, weren't we, by the way the play has been staged. Everything extraneous has been cleared away–it's a bare stage, with virtually no scenery, and very often–especially in the French scenes–the spotlight is literally on the characters. I mean we stand on the stage, in a small pool of light, and we do it: everything is focused on the words and the characters of the men that say them.

Clement McCallin: That's true. The play is suddenly brought back to the *people* in it. Limiting all the other elements, like scenery, liberates the characters, so it becomes a play about people and how they interact–not a lot of stage effects.

Q: What about the staging of the French court scenes? It seems to have a very formal, almost ritualistic quality?

Clement McCallin: That was arrived at by a kind of backwards procedure. We didn't all have long conversations about it. It just gradually happened. I remember when we rehearsed the opening French scene for the first time, we wondered how we were going to do it–would the king have a throne, and so on. Terry said 'Why don't you just try coming on and speaking?' So we did. And the odd thing was, although initially one might have thought, oh, we'll just do it like this for a week or so, and then we'll start introducing elements like thrones–after we *had* been doing it for a while, we didn't want to change it. One stopped wanting some kind of 'placing', because the placing was *them*, it was their inner attitudes that established the scene.

Bernard Brown: It was my first experience for years of that kind of extremely stylised static performance–and it's terribly difficult to do. I remember Terry's giving me a note saying would I try and move my head less, and I thought, Christ! that's the only thing I *am* moving.

Geoffrey Hutchings: That's absolutely true. If you move your head 45 degrees too much, it looks ridiculous. In order to play that court in that space, you have to fine everything down–your range of movement is between the static and the minute.

Clement McCallin: But that formalism does marry up with the kind of verse we are speaking, and the kind of attitudes we're expressing. The thinking of the French is very confined, very rigid, very formal. If you tried to do it naturalistically I think you'd be finished–it would just be a mess.

Geoffrey Hutchings: It's a bit like being at the very back of a Cathedral and watching a priest at the altar: if all his movements were very busy he'd just look ridiculous–and that's how it is on that stage.

Bernard Brown: You're very exposed on that stage.

Geoffrey Hutchings: Yes, but you also have an extraordinarily intimate contact with the audience, you're thrust out into their midst, and they can pick up on the smallest inflection or movement.

Q: That stylisation and formality has been criticised, hasn't it? Some people seem to find it very artificial.

Bernard Brown: Yes, a number of people have said that to me. They don't like what they call 'out-front acting'–the fact that we seem separated on the stage from each other, and that we tend to talk out, to the audience, instead of to each other.

Geoffrey Hutchings: But then the characters are not very unified as a group, are they? The whole point about the French is that they're very divided among themselves.

Bernard Brown: Well, I think it's right. I think it illustrates their lack of cohesion. They are strong, but they're divided in strength. I think their isolation from each other is conveyed very acutely in the night scene, for instance, when we are in separate spotlights. These men don't talk to each other, they can't talk to each other–it's one of their problems as characters and as a court.

Q: Paradoxically though, you seem to me to have brought out very clearly their relationships with each other. What about the French king's relationship with the Dauphin, for instance?

Clement McCallin: Well, that theme is so strong in the other Henry plays–the relationship between Hotspur and Northumberland; the relationship between Hal and Henry IV. And the relationship between the French king and the

Dauphin is there to be found in the lines–the antagonism and irritation between them. It's interesting, for instance, that the king always calls him 'Prince Dauphin'; the first time he uses the word 'son' is to Henry, in the last scene.

Geoffrey Hutchings: The Dauphin is put down by everybody all the time, and especially by his father, who is always curbing him. That's why I play that reaction when Exeter comes on, and talks about the sending of the tennis balls, in front of the king and the court. I think the Dauphin clearly sent the balls without anyone else's knowledge, because he knew the king wouldn't allow it, and because he desperately wants war–he wants to win his spurs, but he's never been near a battle. And that explains his naïvety in the night scene, his eulogy to his horse and so on. He's trying hard to be manly, but he's really like a small boy, and very lonely. Even Orleans, his friend, laughs at him.

Bernard Brown: Yes, and that affects the Constable's attitude to him. The Constable is the professional soldier, and suddenly he's lumbered with this extremely tiresome, inexperienced young man, who also happens to be the king's son–so he can't exactly order him around.

Q: One of the many objections that critics and commentators have had to this play is that the French are ridiculously caricatured. Do you think that, as you play them, the balance between the French and the English is somewhat redressed?

Geoffrey Hutchings: Yes, but then the traditional balance between the English and the French is seen very differently in this production. Henry is not played as a war-monger; he isn't even very confident, or certain about what he's doing. The French *are* confident: and it's not just braggadoccio, they have much to be confident about. They are competent–but they're also divided, and they're also over-romantic about warfare–they want it to be glorious. Their weakness stems from that, not from senility, or effeminacy.

Bernard Brown: They see battle in an archaic way. They're fighting for old glorious chivalric concepts of honour.

Clement McCallin: And they suddenly encounter an army of gritty little men who happen to be fighting for their lives.

Geoffrey Hutchings: But they are fighting for *honour*. I think they're disappointed on the night before Agincourt that the coming battle isn't going to be more glorious, more of a fight – the Dauphin even proposes sending the English dinners and fresh suits, to even up the odds. It's like the heavyweight championship last week, when the American threw a few punches, and was knocked out by the Englishman in the third round, and the Englishman was booed. They want it to be a proper *fight*.

Bernard Brown: And they do seem to have a certain awareness, don't they, before the battle, of what the misery of defeat means? None of them rejoices in the weakness of the English army. That hadn't occurred to me when we started rehearsing the scene before the battle. I was saying all the Constable's lines like trumpet calls. And Terry suggested to me that they might be more sober, slightly more reflective. And I think that's right. The Constable, anyway, as a professional soldier would be aware of the pain and horror of losing a battle. When he says 'A very little, little let us do/And all is done' – I don't think it is a vainglorious boast: I think he sees Death before him. Not his own, of course, the death of the English. But that doesn't particularly make him rejoice.

Q: But the text has been tampered with quite considerably in many of the French scenes, hasn't it? Do you think you could be accused of changing the emphasis of the French scenes by the simple device of altering them?

Clement McCallin: No. I think that what we have done is to find the centre of the French scenes, and strip it down, clarify it.

Bernard Brown: It's true there was a stage at rehearsal when it was all a bit like raffle tickets being thrown up into the air, and you grabbed whatever lines you could. Geoffrey got several of mine, I remember. But, apart from the question of Montjoy, in essence, the parts are very much as they are in the original.

Geoffrey Hutchings: I think we have the right to tamper with the text, if by tampering you mean what we have done. There are virtually no lines written in; we haven't imposed things on the text, we've tried to find the essence of it, as Bernard says, the distillation. And I think we know enough here, in this company, to know what we're doing. That's sounds arrogant, and purists won't like it. But I think we are all steeped in these plays, and in this man's work, and we should be confident that we know what we're doing. In any case, we don't know how accurate the published versions of the plays are.

Bernard Brown: Exactly. I feel sure sometimes that the published versions are every single word that Shakespeare wrote, including revisions, carefully copied down, and that the versions they played may well have differed. In one of our scenes, for instance – before Agincourt – there are two quite clear and separate rhyming couplet endings in the one scene.

Q: Clem, you've been in productions of *Henry V* many times before; you've played Henry yourself. How does this production compare with those?

Clement McCallin: I feel as if I were working on a completely new play. It's a much better, richer play than I realised. I never think about those productions when I'm doing this one – I never feel, oh we used to do so-and-so – why don't they do that? I sit sometimes in the wings and listen to Alan do the breach scene, and I never think about how I did it, how I said a line. Of course when I did it here, it was 1936, Henry was the golden heroic boy, and all you thought about was Lewis Waller, and how he had done it – like a sliver trumpet. I wanted to ring the bells all the time: the only possible questing was in the night scene. But then I was only 22, and I didn't really know what I was doing.

Q: Was it a very large scale production, with masses of extras?

Clement McCallin: No. It was a company of about 35. And there were four extras, who were all Stratford shop assistants, so only two of them came on for matinee performances. I don't think we broke any new ground. It would have been out of the question then to examine the characters as we do. It was rather more a matter of get on there, boy, and do it.

Bernard Brown: And yet, you know, I wonder sometimes if we haven't come full circle. When I acted with Robert Atkins in the early fifties, that was very stylised, very out front. He had seen Irving play, you know, when he was a child of four. I did the two *Henry IV*s with him – he played Falstaff with a deaf aid hidden in his padding. And I played Hamlet for him: 'I won't interfere with your interpretation, my boy,' he said, and then whenever I did a speech, he'd say, 'Ah, but now when Forbes Robertson did it...' That style of acting became very unfashionable and frowned upon afterwards, of course, but maybe now we're moving towards it again. Maybe the naturalistic approach has been over-emphasised – theatrical fashions seem so entrenched for a time, and then suddenly, they've gone. There doesn't seem to me an absolute answer when people criticise the way we play: it's just a constant search, isn't it, for the right approach?

THE ENGLISH ARMY – THE CAPTAINS:
DEREK SMITH – GOWER; BARRIE RUTTER – MACMORRIS;
KEN STOTT – JAMY.

Q: The four captains have been taken by some commentators as almost a joke on Shakespeare's part – the Englishman, Scotsman, Welshman and Irishman got together and then...Do you think the scene between these characters is some kind of comic interlude in the play?

Barrie Rutter: Rubbish. Of course not. I think we *are* funny, I hope we are funny, but that's not the whole point. We're the English army, the solid experienced pros, and how do we behave at that point in the play? We try and kill each other. None of those men is capable of communicating with the others, and all of them – except Gower, who is phlegmatic and understated and English – are violent.

Ken Stott: Well, these men aren't in it for glory, are they? They're in that war because war is their profession, and in order to survive they have to be violent. The violence that erupts between Fluellen and MacMorris is astonishing; there's no real reason for it, it comes out of nowhere, and suddenly MacMorris is trying to cut Fluellen's head off.

Barrie Rutter: It's chilling. If it's done as if they really mean to do each other in, then it's chilling. And of course the fact that MacMorris is Irish, and so Shakespeare's lines about blowing up the town have a modern connotation, makes it all the more chilling. On the night the Queen came, when we got to that bit, I could feel them freezing in their seats. Oh-God-not-in-front-of-our-monarch vibrations came welling up out of the stalls, and swamped me. It was almost impossible to play the scene that night.

Derek Smith: I think we all convey that latent violence and aggression. But I think it's possibly overstated. It's so loud that you can't hear Gower's lines at the end of the scene, which are important. I said that to Terry in rehearsals, but he didn't agree with me.

Barrie Rutter: Well, you've got to make them heard, haven't you? The violence that's unleashed at the end of the scene has got to be virtually unstoppable. It comes just before Henry's speech to the Governor of Harfleur about what his men are going to do to that town if they have to capture it, and his speech carries much more weight if you've just seen them behaving in exactly that manner. They are rough soldiers, and they're not well drilled gentlemen: if MacMorris is going to cut off Fluellen's head he's not going to be stopped by someone muttering.

Q: Clearly, you don't think that the British army of the play is a good solid body of men with a few quaintly eccentric Celts scattered among it…

Ken Stott: Certainly not, the Celts are wild.

Barrie Rutter: Anarchic.

Q: Well, a lot of people have written about the British in the play as if that *was* how Shakespeare meant them. So, if you feel this, that they're violent, and disaffected at this point in the play–what are they later on? Does the army, or the four captains part of it, change?

Barrie Rutter: Well of course in this production we almost are the army. The only other ordinary soldiers are the archers. No extras. Everyone lined up behind the king a recognizable face. And I certainly think that army is shown to change considerably. If we aren't changed, aren't unified, then there's no play.

Ken Stott: It's a difficult area to talk about, because so much of it is a question of reactions. There's no indication of how the army reacts to Henry's approval of Bardolph's execution, for instance. It's a question of knowing the situation those men are in, in the play, and knowing how they might react. It's possible I suppose that they'd could be played going right through the play cheering their heads off and waving the flag, but that doesn't seem to make much sense. Yet obviously we are unified by the time the battle of Agincourt begins, because we win it.

Derek Smith: Not necessarily. Agincourt was lost because of the incompetence of the French commanders.

Q: Do you think then, Derek, that the English army do not become unified in the play?

Derek Smith: I think they do as we play it.

Q: Then do you think that the emphasis placed on that in this production is wrong, that it distorts the text?

Derek Smith: I think there are questions that it still leaves unanswered. It doesn't answer the question—which is a very important moral question that affects the whole of the rest of the play—of whether Henry should be going to war in the first place, and whether he is hypocritical about his motives for doing so. But on the other hand as we rehearsed the later scenes of the play, that feeling of comradeship did seem to emerge naturally, when it hadn't been there before. Just by playing the text, and listening to the text, and reacting to the text, it emerged. So perhaps it has a kind of truth in it. One has to draw a line between the character one is playing, and one's own personal feelings about the play. Gower applauds the king: I am not convinced that enough happens to Henry or his army to make waging the war justifiable.

THE ENGLISH ARMY–THE ARCHERS:
ARTHUR WHYBROW – BATES; DAN MEADEN – WILLIAMS; RICHARD DERRINGTON – COURT.

Q: Bates and Williams (and Court by association with them) are the first characters in the play who really confront the king with the question of his responsibility in war, and the morality of that war. Do you think they get a satisfactory answer from Henry?

Arthur Whybrow: Well *I* don't find it a satisfactory answer. They say to him 'We're going to die tomorrow, whose responsibility is that?'—and he makes a long speech about fathers and sons and masters and servants, and it simply sounds to me like double talk. I suppose Bates accepts his answer, because later on he says he determines to fight lustily for his king, but I don't think he has a clue about what the king means half the time.

Dan Meaden: The central question that Bates and Williams raise in the night scene is–'If the cause be not just...'. They are questioning the validity, the morality of sending men off to die. The king answers as a king: he gives a rather baroque and overwhelming answer. I think most of what he says is lost on Williams totally, and in the end Williams backs down. He's bludgeoned by all those fine intellectual arguments, and those beautifully turned phrases–he's like some poor soul in the witness box being questioned by a crack QC–he doesn't understand, so he semi-capitulates. The spirit of Williams' question is not answered by Henry, not then, anyway. I think it's answered to Williams' somewhat bewildered satisfaction, but not to mine.

Richard Derrington: I don't think that any of those characters are in any state to be able to listen to that kind of talk anyhow. And that's interesting in itself–that Henry doesn't yet understand how to talk to his army. If he did he wouldn't be making speeches like that at the moment when they're all obviously desperate, cold, terrified of the dawn, and convinced they're going to die the next day. Court is clearly so numb with terror he can hardly speak. All he can do is watch the sun come up.

Q: What about the later sequences of the play? We see the army almost mutinous and disaffected at the end of the first half. Then we see Williams and Bates questioning the war in the night scene, and being somewhat cynical about the king and his ransom. Then, by the end of the Crispin's Day speech, they seem to be unified behind him. Does that dramatic development convince you?

Dan Meaden: I don't think cynical is the right word. I think earlier in the play it's clear that the army is not behind Henry, not in the real sense. He executes Bardolph, after all, for doing something–plundering–that was widely regarded as every soldier's right. Then, in spite of the fact that he knows that his army is sick and in retreat he makes a rhetorical speech to Montjoy and says that, nonetheless, the English will meet the French. That's the end of the first half of the play. In the night scene we're browbeaten, and we're afraid. But we're old soldiers who are sceptical about those in authority, not cynics. After Crispin's day that scepticism does change, and I think it's a genuine transition. I think Henry transforms the army and its attitudes by an amazing piece of acting. He bucks us up. He has to. And then in the speech after that, when Montjoy is present again, he seems to find a real language, and a real way of talking to his army and being one with them.

Richard Derrington: Well, there's a catalyst there isn't there? Montjoy comes on just at the moment when the English are beginning to be roused, and that is the last necessary trigger, for us, and for Henry. Suddenly there's a foreigner in our midst: that's what finally unites us.

Q: One of the critics made the point that this Henry learns from his soldiers, as well as they from him. Do you think that's true? Or does he just learn to put on a better act?

Dan Meaden: I think there is a change, a genuine one. I think to an extent he's is shown to be still putting on an act in the Crispin's Day speech. All that stuff about well, if you don't want to fight this battle you can leave. That's the oldest ruling class ploy in the book. Soldiers aren't going to walk away from the Normandy beaches are they?

Arthur Whybrow: Where are you supposed to go if you did walk off, anyway? Slap into the enemy.

Dan Meaden: But after that there is a difference. When Henry offers Williams the glove full of money, for instance. As we do that, I don't accept it. Now why not? It depends on how you read the text, obviously, but it seems to me that Williams starts by beginning to grovel–'Your majesty came not like yourself' and then he pulls himself up. He almost *demands* pardon of Henry, and he won't be bought off with the money. I don't think he would do that if Henry were not more than a simple authority figure at that point. I think perhaps Williams recognises an honesty in him which is very like his own.

THE ENGLISH ARMY–THE FAMILY:
ANTHONY NAYLOR–CLARENCE; STEPHEN JENN–
GLOUCESTER; REGINALD JESSUP–WESTMORELAND.

Q: In the way that this production is staged and cast, the king's immediate family–his uncle Exeter, his cousin Westmoreland, and his two brothers, Clarence and Gloucester–become a very identifiable family group on stage. Do you think that helps the play?

Anthony Naylor: Yes I think it does. As we do it, each person stands for many others like him: Jamy is all the Scots, Macmorris is all the Irishmen. And the different groups each represent different social strata. The play is no longer about a king and his faceless thousands; the audience gets to know all the individuals on the stage, and I think, I *hope* that that enhances their interest. The lords are normally rather a problem in a Shakespeare play – if anyone is faceless and unidentifiable, it is them. As we do it, Henry's family – who represent the nobility – are clearly defined. They have relationships with each other, and with the king, that affect the course of the play. I think we have made the family into a group of human beings, with a strong family identity.

Q: Is that helped by the fact that, as Terry Hands has cast it, all the brothers, Henry included, have a strong family resemblance – the red hair, for instance?

Anthony Naylor: Well, red hair *is* such an identifying factor, such a mark. It means you always get picked out first and recognised as a group of people. But there is greater resemblance between the four of us that that – we are all tall, even facially there are certain similarities: it seems to me that we become identifiable as brothers, with physical resemblances and differences that mirror the distinctions in our characters.

Stephen Jenn: People are a bit sceptical about it, when you tell them what a small part you have. I only have about four lines in *Henry V*, but I think that they are enough to give you a sense of Gloucester, and the way he differs from Clarence. He is the one who needs the most reassuring, the one who says 'I hope they do not come upon us now'. The one that Henry is the first to comfort and console in the night scene.

Anthony Naylor: And Clarence is the brother who is closest to Henry. That has already been established in the earlier plays, and we carried it through in *Henry V*. Their father tells Clarence that he is Henry's favourite brother, in *Henry IV Part Two*. It seemed right, therefore, that in this play, Clarence should be the one who is physically always at Henry's side. He is the one who supplies the friendship – if you like, the back-up support. He is his bodyguard in the Southampton scenes, when the other members of the family are marking the traitors; he is the one who helps Henry dress, put on his surcoat and so on; he is the one who, when Henry has been so thrown, emotionally, at the end of Southampton, knows how to handle him, who knows how to nudge him back on course–that's why I hand him the surcoat, and help him on with it at that point: it's a reminder to him, if you like, of the role that he has to assume.

Reginald Jessup: I think Westmoreland is somewhat on the edge of that family group. He's an older man, like Exeter, and he has been completely loyal to Henry IV. In this play I think he is somewhat unsure of Henry, of this unknown quantity who is the new king at the beginning of the play. I tried to carry through the apprehension that Westmoreland obviously feels at the end of *Part Two* when Hal's father has died, about what kind of a king the new man will make–he is worried about the fate of the Lord Chief Justice and so on. The man is not very fleshed out, and I didn't find it easy to get started on him. But I think he is a professional soldier, very straight, very reliable, the first to lament the fact that they're short of men at Agincourt, and, with Exeter, very worried about the way Henry handles the traitors at Southampton. He can't understand why he places himself in such a dangerous position, and why he gets so worked up emotionally about Scroop's betrayal. I think Westmoreland must be worried about what kind of a leader in war that man is going to make, after that scene. He could be foolhardy–a man who would get others killed as well as himself, and a trained soldier would be worried by that.

Stephen Jenn: Maybe that feeling of Henry's being something of an unknown quantity was helped by the very rehearsal situation itself. When we all met for the first time Alan Howard was in the position of leading the company, and we didn't know him, we didn't know what kind of performance he would give, and we were strangers, we didn't have a relationship with him.

Anthony Naylor: We were all strangers to each other, with a few exceptions. Now we've been playing the play for as long as we have, that has changed somewhat. I know Stephen, and I know Charles Dance, who is playing the third brother, John of Lancaster in the other plays–it's possible to build up a sense of family intimacy with each other. There are

...ut generally orderly atmos-here.

It was, in fact, just like the ...ld days. The football, however, ...nly occasionally matched the ...etting, a state of affairs for ...hich the elements were largely ...esponsible.

The strong wind and hard ...round made accurate football ...ifficult, and there were few ...onnected series of passes until ...ate in the second half when a ...risk shower took some of the ...one from the pitch.

Manchester United won be-...ause they took two early ...hances presented to them by ...esitancy in the Leeds defence. ...anchester were always the ...uicker, sharper side, more ...exible in every way, and far ...etter prepared to react to the ...nexpected.

Leeds, by contrast, were a ...onderous disappointment. Their ...ull-backs, Reaney and Hampton, ...ooked vulnerable whenever ...anchester attacked down the ...anks, and the uncertainty soon ...pread to McQueen and Madeley, ...oth of whom had mixed after-...oons.

In midfield, too, Manchester ...ad a considerable edge. Macari ...nd McIlroy had more ideas ...han their Leeds counterparts, ...hile Coppell and Hill, apart ...rom the threat they posed in ...ttack, tackled back effectively towards the interval that they put their opponents under proper pressure. With McQueen up in attack and Cherry always ready to try a shot, Manchester were perhaps lucky to survive this period; but their overall superiority at this stage was undeniable.

For 20 minutes of the second half Manchester looked like cruising quietly home. With the wind at their backs they fired in a succession of shots, produc-ing some fine saves by Stewart.

Leeds were looking a beaten side when Cherry sent Jordan away on the left side of the penalty area. There were three Manchester defenders in attend-ance, and little need for Nicholl to bring Jordan down in a fit of misplaced enthusiasm.

Stepney got a hand to Clarke's penalty shot, but Leeds—sud-denly and unexpectedly—were back in the match.

It would, however, have been a travesty of justice if Manchester had been cheated of their due reward, and although McQueen coming forward in attack once caught the opposing defence dangerously square, Manchester survived without too much trouble. Indeed they could easily have had a penalty them-selves at the other end which would more accurately have reflected the difference between the two teams.

In the end, then, a more exciting match than seemed ...ikely early on. Manchester ...horoughly deserved their vic-...ory, and if they can produce ...his sort of form at Wembley I ...ave a feeling that with nothing ...se to worry about they may ...ake amends for last season's ...isappointment.

Weather: showery. Pitch: firm.
Leeds United (4-4-2). Stewart;
...eaney, McQueen, Madeley, Hampton;
...arrie, Cherry, F. Gray (sub. Lorimer,
...5min.), E. Gray; Clarke, Jordan.
Manchester United (4-4-2): Stepney;

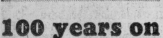

Jack Rover
I am the bold Thunder!

100 years on

THE SUCCESS of Wild Oats, the Royal Shakespeare Company's inspired revival of John O'Keefe's wild eighteenth-century comedy, marks a happy coincidence for its leading player, Alan Howard. Backstage at the Piccadilly Theatre last week, after the opening of the public-demanded West End transfer, he told me of a touching ancestral discovery.

Howard is the great-grandson of the actor-manager Edward Compton, founder and mainstay of the Compton Comedy Company. For years, he had the above drawing of his forebear proudly displayed on his mantelpiece—never understanding the inscription: "I am the bold Thunder." While reading the play (unstaged since 1886) for the RSC, he discovered to his amazement that it is the first line of his own role, the strolling player Jack Rover. Records were dug up, and sure enough Compton himself played Jack Rover at Stratford in 1882 and in London the following year.

Howard felt "spooked" by the whole thing, especially when Mander and Mitchenson, the theatre historians, presented him with a facsimile of the playbill for Compton's first London performance. It was almost to the day 100 years before the date of Howard's birth. Still and all, his family is not otherwise without distinction; he is great-nephew to both Fay Compton and Compton Mackenzie, and on his father's side nephew of Leslie Howard. With relations like that, who needs managers?

even jokes between us as actors, and these can become like family jokes, the kind of nuances that you always get between brothers, within the context of the plays.

THE UNDERBELLY OF THE ARMY:
TIM WYLTON–BARDOLPH; RICHARD MOORE–PISTOL; PHILIP DUNBAR–NYM; MAUREEN PRYOR–MISTRESS QUICKLY.

Q: With the exception of Nym, who hasn't appeared before, you all play characters in *Henry V* who have come through from the earlier plays. You're all much older now, for one thing: how do you feel about your characters at the start of this play–are they very different?

Tim Wylton: I think we're all dead. Our lives are over, but our bodies go on.

Richard Moore: That's true–we've lost Falstaff, for one thing. He's about to die, so the core, the leadership of the group has gone; we have somehow to reorganise ourselves and start again. So we all go off to war, with the same intentions that Falstaff had in the earlier plays–good pickings; plunder.

Tim Wylton: But there's something empty about the whole project. *Henry V* is a winter play, there's a feeling that these characters, these elements should have died off like weeds. They can't cope with the climate of this play.

Maureen Pryor: There's a sense of failure, of making do, right from the beginning. When Pistol and I enter in our first scene we've come straight from our marriage–Bardolph showers us with confetti–but even that marriage is a second-best thing: Mistress Quickly was so clearly in love with Falstaff–the great moment in her life was in the Dolphin chamber when he promised to marry her. And now she's married Falstaff's Ancient, his understudy if you like–the other swaggerer. She takes him because she can't have Falstaff.

Q: Falstaff may be dead–or dying–and we may never see him in this play, but the influence still seems enormously felt, particularly by this group of characters.

Richard Moore: Well, we are that world, Falstaff's world, the Boar's Head world, which is suddenly uprooted to the fields of France. But the fact that he is no longer present alters our roles and our relationships—in the earlier plays, Pistol seems to represent a kind of external anarchy. He comes smashing into the Boar's Head, smashing into Shallow's orchard in Gloucestershire. In this play Pistol has to become the leader of the group, and Shakespeare brings Nym in as a foil to Pistol very much as Pistol was to Falstaff.

Maureen Pryor: But there's still an enormous gap, a gap that is never filled. And we're all very definite about where the responsibility lies. Falstaff is dying, and I say, 'The king hath killed his heart'.

Tim Wylton: I just feel that once Falstaff has gone we almost cease to exist, we're all finished. Bardolph should never have gone to France: he should just have died off stage, about three days after Falstaff.

Q: But on the other hand there seems to be something about these characters that makes them survivors, for a time, anyway. Pistol, particularly. The others may die, but he survives. At the very end, when we last see him, he's still planning ways to turn his afflictions to advantage—'And patches will I get unto these cudgell'd scars/And swear I got them in the Gallia wars'. Did you really feel that they were as finished as all that?

Richard Moore: I suppose he is a survivor of a kind. I think Pistol is full of optimism at the beginning, for instance. He's married Mistress Quickly, and he obviously thinks he's onto a good thing. I mean, she presumably owns the Boar's Head—I think he's already envisaging a chain of Holiday Inns...

Tim Wylton: But once they go to war, they've had it. They're like dinosaurs—creatures from another era. They're the underbelly of the war, and the underbelly is going to be cut out.

Philip Dunbar: I think that's true: the only world that Nym can function in is a dead world—there's no place for it in the new order.

Q: Do you think that Shakespeare has made these characters aware of that—aware that they're not a part of the new society Henry seems to be creating? They've had several warnings in the earlier plays, haven't they?

Maureen Pryor: No, I don't think they're made to realise—but they are affected. The way we all cling to each other, to our little world. We're very interdependent, and we're very afraid. We're in danger of losing our living or our lives all the time.

Philip Dunbar: Well, we're all cowards—the men anyway. We have to cling together for protection. Pistol is supposed to be our leader, and he's the biggest coward of all of us.

Tim Wylton: The Boy points that out, of course. He's terribly important. He sees how weak and empty we are. He's younger than we are–he sees us with very clear eyes. He knows we're finished, and he's planning to leave us.

Q: You are cowardly, of course. And yet there's a moment when Pistol anyway, is quite brave–when he pleads for Bardolph...

Richard Moore: Yes, he does do that. And it is very brave. He goes to what are, actually, extraordinary lengths. He tries to bribe Fluellen to intercede for Bardolph, and Fluellen is a captain. He's laying his own life on the line when he does that, and he must be aware of it.

Q: His behaviour at that point arouses a lot of sympathy, I think. So does Bardolph's fate, and so, in a way, does your whole attitude to war–the fear, and the skiving. Do you feel people sympathise with these characters?

Richard Moore: Yes. I do: I think we represent a line–a type–that goes back through every war you can ever think of. Being afraid, but trying to survive, trying to make a bit on the side, seeing what you can get out of it. In many ways we're the British Tommy–and people do respond to that. I met someone the other night who had been to see the show, and they said, 'Oh, it was so marvellous, when you were all getting ready to fight at Agincourt', and I said, 'You mean the Crispin's day speech?' And they said, 'Well, yes that's terrific, but what I really liked was the moment when you all had to get up in the morning, when you were rolling up your blankets, and fixing your equipment...'

Q: In this production, of course, Nym, Bardolph and Pistol are very much part of the English army. You are the ones who don't go over the breach after Henry's speech; Pistol is there for Crispin's day; there for the killing of the French prisoners. We see you as individuals, and we see you in the army. How did you feel about that element in the production?

Philip Dunbar: I think that it's one of the triumphs of this production–and something that no-one seems to have commented on–that the army you see on stage is composed of real people–every single one of them has been established already, and the audience knows them. They know us, they know the Boy, they know the four captains and Williams and Bates and Court. They're all real recognizable *men*–the army isn't just noblemen and 30 spear carriers...*we* are the army. It becomes a real force in the play.

Richard Moore: And it has the effect of making the divisions within the army very clear; you know its not just an anonymous group. There's a mad Irishman, there's Pistol, who's a turkey-cock, but who shuts up when he's in the presence of a bigger turkey-cock. You get a real sense of the pecking order.

Tim Wylton: You can see the three different levels of the army when they start out–the king and the nobles, the ordinary soldiers like Bates and Williams, and the ragged underbelly, which is us. It's also economy, of course, think of the saving on all those spear carriers' salaries...

Q: The army changes its character, it seems to me, during the course of the evening. Perhaps because each individual is real and established one gets a very strong feeling of the disunity in the army before Agincourt–they aren't just an anonymous group of men obeying orders and rushing happily over the breach at Henry's behest. And this feeling is strongest at the end of the first half, when first Bardolph is executed, then Henry forbids plunder. The army becomes almost mutinous at this moment. The death of Bardolph assumes an enormous importance, and the decision to execute him is very clearly made Henry's. How did you feel about that sequence when you were rehearsing?

Tim Wylton: Well I think it *is* a moment of enormous importance. And the advantage of doing it like that is that it brings all the old relationships of the previous plays flooding back onto the stage. If he can actually do that, actually order Bardolph's death – you realise the change that there has been in Hal.

Richard Moore: And it's a link–a very strong link–with things we've seen before. In *Part One*, for instance, we've seen Hal perform the mock hanging of Bardolph in the Boar's Head, when he says 'No, if rightly taken, halter', and hangs Bardolph with a scarf. But now he actually does it. He's given him the warning about his likely fate, and now he's the person who turns that prophecy into reality...

Tim Wylton: The thing that worries me about all that is–what does that moment mean to people who don't know, or haven't seen, the other plays? They must just think what's this big deal about that little fellow who only had two scenes...

Richard Moore: I don't know how we think of issues and

implications like that when we're doing it anyway. Then we're just playing from moment to moment.

Philip Dunbar: That's true. It sounds conscious when we talk about it now, but when we're on-stage it's just the character, and that particular moment.

Q: But don't you think about those questions and implications when you're rehearsing?

Philip Dunbar: Well I suppose we do, to an extent. I remember Terry talking to us after one of the Dress Rehearsals, and he said, 'This isn't the production that I intended to produce. You have evolved the style of this performance'. Looking back, maybe we did. In a way.

THE WOMEN:
LUDMILA MIKAËL–KATHERINE (1st night–June 1975);
CAROLLE ROUSSEAU–KATHERINE (June and thereafter);
YVONNE COULETTE–ALICE.

Q: Do you think it made a difference to your scenes having French speaking actresses playing the parts?

Yvonne Coulette: Yes, I think it made a difference for us, and I hope it made a difference for the audience. Someone told me that it was the first time they had seen a Kate and an Alice who seemed to *think* in French. And that their foreignness, their separation from the other characters, and their distance from Henry at the beginning of the wooing scene, became all the more real.

Ludmila Mikaël: I felt it made a great difference. I was actually working in another country, in England, for the first time, and I was playing one of the only two characters who speak French in an English play. I had the strange feeling that I was defending my language in front of an English audience, which is somewhat what Katherine has to do in her last scene with Henry.

Q: What do you feel about the wooing scene? Is it a wooing, or just the final maneouvrings of a political match?

Ludmila Mikaël: It is not just a political match. There is a development in it. I think Katherine is a match for Henry, in both senses–she is as strong a woman as he is a man, although she is young and very inexperienced. She is very adept with words, she is good at verbal games; she asks him a very challenging question—when she says, 'Is it possible that I should love the enemy of France'. Because she is strong, perhaps, something happens between them in the scene—they fall in love, whatever you want to say, but they reach each other in spite of the fact that they don't speak the same language.

Yvonne Coulette: I think maybe their difficulties over language is one of the things that brings them together. They cannot help laughing when the other mangles a French word or an English phrase...

Carolle Rousseau: It has to be fairly cold in the beginning when they meet: they are strangers, there are barriers between them. She is mourning the death of her relatives, that his soldiers have killed in battle. But I think those barriers break down in the scene. Through laughter, maybe, yes. Because you do not have to speak the same language to laugh at the same things.

Q: Did you find it very different working in an English Company?

Ludmila Mikaël: So different, so different from the Comédie Française. Your actors work so hard, they train their voice, they do movement, we don't do anything of that. In France if an actor is not working, he rests, he walks up and down the corridors. He does not practice. But you practice, you work, all the time over here...

HENRY V

William Shakespeare

Cast list for the Royal Shakespeare Theatre Centenary Production

Chorus	Emrys James
THE ENGLISH	
Archbishop of Canterbury	Derek Smith
Bishop of Ely	Trevor Peacock
King Henry V	Alan Howard
Humphrey Duke of Gloucester } *brothers to*	Stephen Jenn
Thomas Duke of Clarence } *the king*	Anthony Naylor
Duke of Exeter *uncle to the king*	Philip Brack
Earl of Cambridge	Barrie Rutter
Lord Scroop	Dan Meaden
Sir Thomas Grey	Arthur Whybrow
Earl of Westmoreland	Reginald Jessup
Corporal Bardolph	Tim Wylton
Corporal Nym	Philip Dunbar
Ancient Pistol	Richard Moore
Boy	Peter Bourke
Mistress Quickly	Maureen Pryor

Gower	*Captains in*	Derek Smith
Fluellen	*King Henry's*	Trevor Peacock
Macmorris	*army*	Barrie Rutter
Jamy		Ken Stott
Williams	*Soldiers in*	Dan Meaden
Bates	*King Henry's*	Arthur Whybrow
Court	*army*	Richard Derrington
Sir Thomas Erpingham		Reginald Jessup

THE FRENCH

King Charles VI of France	Clement McCallin
Dauphin *his son*	Geoffrey Hutchings
Katharine *his daughter*	Ludmila Mikaël, Carolle Rousseau*
Duke of Orleans	Philip Dunbar
The Constable of France	Bernard Brown
Montjoy *Herald of the French*	Oliver Ford-Davies
Monsieur le Fer	Tim Wylton
Alice *a Lady-in-Waiting*	Yvonne Coulette

Musicians Gordon Bennett Nigel Garvey William Grant Roger Hellyer Peter Morris Robert Pritchard Ian Reynolds Gareth Richards David Statham Michael Tubbs Robin Weatherall

Directed by Terry Hands
Designed by Farrah
Music by Guy Woolfenden
Lighting by Stewart Leviton
Assistant to the Director Ian Judge
Stage Manager David Noble
Deputy Stage Manager Mark ap Robert
Assistant Stage Manager Louise Horswill

*Ludmila Mikaël (from 1st night until June 1975.) Carolle Rousseau (thereafter).

HENRY V

NOTES ON THE TEXT

The following is the working text of the play, as used in Terry Hands' production for the Royal Shakespeare Company.

Passages which have been cut from the original have been marked in italics. Certain speeches, and some scenes, have been transposed from their original order. Where this is the case there is an explanatory note from the director. In some cases characters in the original play have been cut out, and their speeches given to others. Montjoy, for instance, in several of the scenes in the French court and camp, has been given parts of the speeches of Rambures, Grandpré and others, who did not appear in the production. Where this occurs the text is printed as it was spoken in performance, and there is an explanatory note from the director.

The act and scene division is that used in performance: there are two acts, with an interval between them.

All notes on text, staging, and production are from the director, Terry Hands, unless otherwise stated. When they are from actors, the performer's name preceeds the note, with the name of the character he played in brackets after.

All stage directions and line numberings refer to the production.

SALLY BEAUMAN.

ACT I

*The actors are on stage, in rehearsal clothes, as
the audience enters the theatre. As the performance
begins they gradually take up their positions, sitting
or lying on the stage. The Chorus comes forward*

CHORUS

O for a Muse of fire, that would ascend
The brightest heaven of invention,
A kingdom for a stage, princes to act,
And monarchs to behold the swelling scene!
Then should the warlike Harry, like himself,
Assume the port of Mars, and at his heels,
Leashed in like hounds, should famine, sword, and
    fire
Crouch for employment. But pardon, gentles all,
The flat unraised spirits that hath dared
On this unworthy scaffold to bring forth   10
So great an object. Can this cockpit hold
The vasty fields of France? Or may we cram
Within this wooden O the very casques
That did affright the air at Agincourt?
O, pardon! since a crooked figure may
Attest in little place a million,
And let us, ciphers to this great account,
On your imaginary forces work;

The opening of the play: The Chorus of *Henry V* states the principles of
Shakespeare's theatre: its methods and aspirations. Starting from a simple
wooden platform a group of actors will endeavour to stimulate the imagination
of an audience. Between them a play will evolve, and its strengths and
weaknesses will be the measure of that collaboration. The audience invariably
begins from scratch. They are dressed normally. So perhaps might be the
actors.

Accordingly the company began literally as 'flat, unraised spirits', in their
rehearsal clothes on a completely bare stage. As the audience gathered from
half an hour before the start of the play, so too did the actors. It was essential
that the actor should be made as aware of *his* function within the collaboration,
as the audience were to be of theirs.

Suppose within the girdle of these walls
Are now confined two mighty monarchies,   20
Whose high uprearèd and abutting fronts
The perilous narrow ocean parts asunder.
Piece out our imperfections with your thoughts:
Into a thousand parts divide one man,
And make imaginary puissance.
Think, when we talk of horses, that you see them
Printing their proud hoofs i'th'receiving earth;
For 'tis your thoughts that now must deck our kings,
Carry them here and there, jumping o'er times,
Turning th'accomplishment of many years   30
Into an hour-glass: for the which supply,
Admit me Chorus to this history,
Who Prologue-like your humble patience pray,
Gently to hear, kindly to judge, our play.

Scene I

The Chorus moves back upstage, and the
Archbishop of Canterbury and the Bishop of Ely
come forward

CANTERBURY

My lord, *I'll tell you.* That self bill is urged
Which in th'eleventh year of the last King's reign
Was like, and had indeed against us passed,
But that the scambling and unquiet time
Did push it out of farther question.

ELY

But how, may lord, shall we resist it now?

CANTERBURY

It must be thought on. If it pass against us,
We lose the better half of our possession;
For all the temporal lands which men devout
By testament have given to the Church   10
Would they strip from us; being valued thus–
As much as would maintain, to the King's honour,
Full fifteen earls, and fifteen hundred knights,
Six thousand and two hundred good esquires;

And, to relief *of lazars and weak age,*
Of indigent faint souls past corporal toil,
A hundred almshouses right well supplied;
And, to the coffers of the King beside,
A thousand pounds by th'year. Thus runs the bill.

ELY

This would drink deep.

CANTERBURY   'Twould drink the cup and all.

ELY

But what prevention?   20

CANTERBURY

The King is full of grace and fair regard.

ELY

And a true lover of the holy Church.

CANTERBURY

The courses of his youth promised it not.
The breath no sooner left his father's body
But that his wildness, mortified in him,
Seemed to die too. Yea, at that very moment,
Consideration like an angel came
And whipped th'offending Adam out of him,
Leaving his body as a paradise
T'envelop and contain celestial spirits.
Never was such a sudden scholar made;
Never came reformation in a flood
With such a heady currance scouring faults;
Nor never Hydra-headed wilfulness
So soon did lose his seat, and all at once,
As in this King.

23 following: The cut here is apparently large.

In fact it is only a section. Basically one thing is being said, however long it takes to say: that the wastrel Hal has become saintly.

The thought is naive, and not born out by the end of *Henry IV Part II.* Furthermore it is belied by what is to follow. One might argue that the speech is deliberately ironical, or elaborately over-stated to make us re-examine the real Henry V in the light of his publicity. It seems a peculiarly un-dramatic idea to spend a whole play disproving or approving one character's first scene assessment.

Furthermore it is not well written. It is over written. Shakespeare could write badly, especially for special occasions. This may be one of them. Accordingly we treated it as a later insertion and cut it.

ELY   *We are blessèd in the change.*

CANTERBURY
Hear him but reason in divinity,
And all-admiring, with an inward wish,
You would desire the King were made a prelate.
Hear him debate of commonwealth affairs,
You would say it hath been all in all his study.
List his discourse of war, and you shall hear
A fearful battle rendered you in music.
Turn him to any cause of policy,
The Gordian knot of it he will unloose,
Familiar as his garter; that, when he speaks,
The air, a chartered libertine, is still,
And the mute wonder lurketh in men's ears
To steal his sweet and honeyed sentences.
So that the art and practic part of life
Must be the mistress to this theoric—
Which is a wonder how his grace should glean it,
Since his addiction was to courses vain,
His companies unlettered, rude, and shallow,
His hours filled up with riots, banquets, sports,
And never noted in him any study,
Any retirement, any sequestration,
From open haunts and popularity.

ELY
The strawberry grows underneath the nettle,
And wholesome berries thrive and ripen best
Neighboured by fruit of baser quality:
And so the Prince obscured his contemplation
Under the veil of wildness, which, no doubt,
Grew like the summer grass, fastest by night,
Unseen, yet crescive in his faculty.

CANTERBURY
It must be so, for miracles are ceased.
And therefore we must needs admit the means
How things are perfected.

ELY   But, my good lord,
How now for mitigation of this bill

Urged against the Church? Doth his majesty   30
Incline to it, or no?
CANTERBURY   He seems indifferent,
Or rather swaying more upon our part
Than cherishing th'exhibiters against us;
For I have made an offer to his majesty–
Upon our spiritual Convocation,
And in regard of causes now in hand,
Which I have opened to his grace at large
As touching France–to give a greater sum
Than ever at one time the clergy yet
Did to his predecessors part withal.
ELY
How did this offer seem received, my lord?
CANTERBURY
With good acceptance of his majesty
Save that there was not time enough to hear,   40
As I perceived his grace would fain have done,
The severals and unhidden passages
Of his true titles to some certain dukedoms,
And generally to the crown and seat of France,
Derived from Edward, his great-grandfather.
ELY
What was the impediment that broke this off?
CANTERBURY
The French ambassador upon that instant
Craved audience, and the hour, I think, is come
To give him hearing. Is it four o'clock?
ELY
It is
CANTERBURY
Then go we in to know his embassy;

30 In Shakespeare's text this line reads 'Urged by the Commons'. It was changed for greater clarity: the bill being discussed is urged by the Commons against the Church. It is very important for the audience to follow this section of the play, and they are not helped by the text, which is very baroque.
45 following: All these lines were kept in early performances, but it became clear that they slowed up the action unnecessarily: the audience is more interested in what will come of the further discussions between Henry and Canterbury, than they are in court etiquette and the French Ambassador. He *will* arrive; he can be talked about and introduced properly then.

Which I could with a ready guess declare
Before the Frenchman speak a word of it.

ELY

I'll wait upon you, and I long to hear it.

Scene II

Henry gets up from where he has been sitting,
towards the back of the stage, and comes down
to greet Canterbury

KING HENRY

Where is my gracious lord of Canterbury?

EXETER

Not here in presence.

KING HENRY

Send for him, good uncle.

WESTMORELAND

Shall we call in th'ambassador, my liege?

KING HENRY

Not, yet, my cousin; we would be resolved,
Before we hear him, of some things of weight
That task our thoughts, concerning us and France.

CANTERBURY

God and His angels guard your sacred throne,
And make you long become it!

KING HENRY   Sure, we thank you.

My learned lord, we pray you to proceed,
And justly and religiously unfold
Why the law Salie that they have in France
Or should or should not bar us in our claim.
And God forbid, my dear and faithful lord,
That you should fashion, wrest, or bow your reading,
Or nicely charge your understanding soul   10
With opening titles miscreate, whose right

Scene II 2–3 God and his angels... Canterbury turns upstage to greet the
King at this point, and as he does so, he opens his jacket to reveal a pectoral
cross. On turning back to the audience they witness the first costume element
since the play began. It is now the second scene. Step by step the play grows
toward conventional presentation.

i

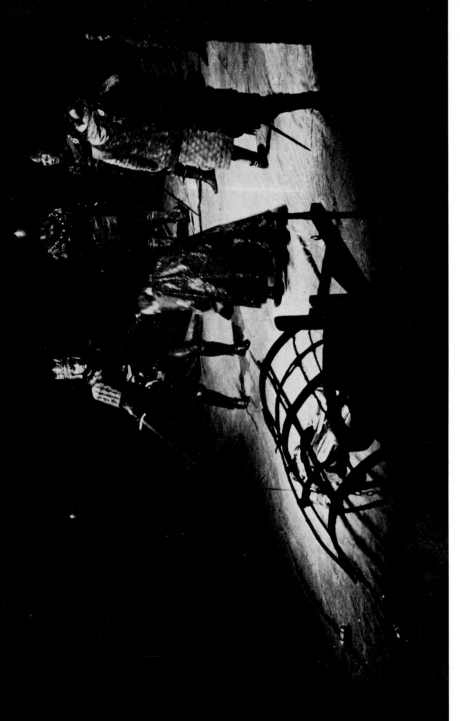

v

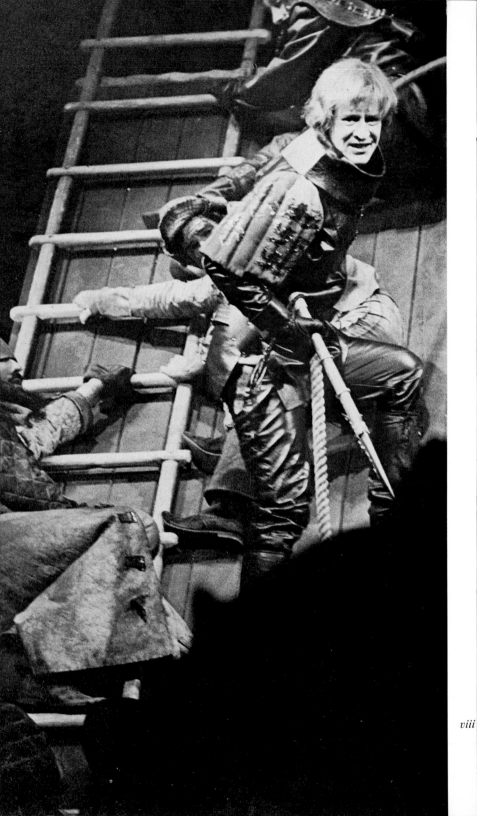

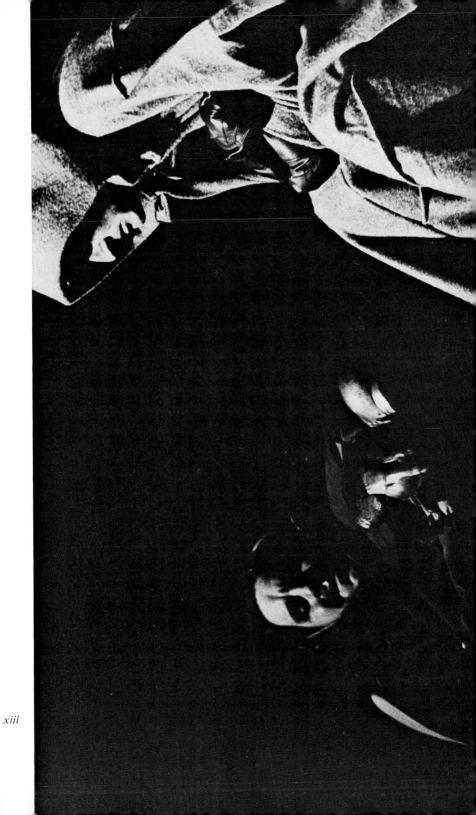

xv

xvi

xx

xxi

x

INDEX OF PHOTOGRAPHS

I. The night before Agincourt: Alan Howard as Henry V.

II. Farrah's set, showing the canopy.

III. Farrah's set, showing the canopy lowered.

IV. The set after the battle of Agincourt.

V. The arrival of the Dauphin's tennis balls. This opening sequence of the play was performed with actors in rehearsal clothes. Ultimately the French Ambassador was the only character to appear in costume in this scene. When this photograph was taken, at an early preview, the Archbishop also wore costume. Later this was changed. Alan Howard as Henry, Philip Brack as Exeter, Derek Smith as the Archbishop of Canterbury, Oliver Ford-Davies as the Ambassador, Anthony Naylor as Clarence.

VI. The Welsh and the English captains: Trevor Peacock as Fluellen, Derek Smith as Gower.

VII. Emrys James as the Chorus.

VIII. The breach at Harfleur. Alan Howard as Henry.

IX. In the shelter of the breach: "The knocks are too hot". Richard Moore as Pistol, Tim Wylton as Bardolph, Philip Dunbar as Nym, Peter Bourke as the Boy.

X. After the fall of Harfleur: "Use mercy to them all". Philip Brack as Exeter, Alan Howard as Henry.

XI. Katherine, the Princess of France and Alice. Ludmila Mikaël and Yvonne Coulette. Ludmila Mikaël, sociétaire of the Comédie Française, played Katherine from the first night until June 1975.

XII. The English army in the fields of France: Derek Smith as Gower, Arthur Whybrow as Bates, Trevor Peacock as Fluellen, Richard Derrington as Court.

XIII. The English camp the night before Agincourt. Richard Moore as Pistol, Alan Howard as Henry.

XIV. The English camp the night before Agincourt. Alan Howard as Henry, Arthur Whybrow as Bates, Dan Meaden as Williams.

XV. The French camp on the morning of Agincourt: "England shall couch down in fear and yield." Philip Dunbar as Orleans, Bernard Brown as the Constable of France, Geoffrey Hutchings as the Dauphin, Oliver Ford-Davies (front) as Montjoy the herald.

XVI. The French on the morning of Agincourt. Philip Dunbar as Orleans, Bernard Brown as the Constable of France, Geoffrey Hutchings as the Dauphin.

XVII. Oliver Ford-Davies as Montjoy, and Clement McCallin as the King of France.

XVIII. The English on the morning of Agincourt–the Crispin's Day speech. Philip Brack as Exeter, Peter Bourke as the Boy, Alan Howard as Henry.

XIX. Montjoy's visit to the English camp immediately before the battle. The English army, standing: Richard Moore as Pistol, Barrie Rutter as Macmorris, the Irish captain, Philip Brack as Exeter, Stephen Jenn as Gloucester, Anthony Naylor as Clarence, Reginald Jessup as the Earl of Westmoreland. Foreground, Alan Howard as Henry. Oliver Ford-Davies as Montjoy.

XX. The battle of Agincourt itself. Pistol, with the Boy as his interpreter captures M. Le Fer. Richard Moore as Pistol, Peter Bourke as the Boy, Tim Wylton as M. Le Fer.

XXI. "I was not angry since I came to France": the killing of the Boy. Anthony Naylor as Clarence, Trevor Peacock as Fluellen, Richard Moore as Pistol, Alan Howard as Henry, Barrie Rutter as Macmorris, Derek Smith as Gower, Peter Bourke as the Boy.

XXII. After the news of victory but before the reading of the French dead. Alan Howard as Henry.

XXIII. The reading of the English dead. Philip Brack as Exeter, Stephen Jenn as Gloucester, Alan Howard as Henry, Anthony Naylor as Clarence.

XXIV. Henry's wooing of the Princess of France. Ludmila Mikaël as Katherine, Alan Howard as Henry.

XXV. Terry Hands, Director of Henry V, in rehearsal.

XXVI. 27th June 1975, the Gala performance of Henry V, attended by Her Majesty the Queen, and the Duke of Edinburgh, seen here with Terry Hands, meeting Alan Howard and the rest of the cast backstage after the performance.

Suits not in native colours with the truth;
For God doth know how many now in health
Shall drop their blood in approbation
Of what your reverence shall incite us to.
Therefore take heed how you impawn our person,
How you awake our sleeping sword of war
We charge you, in the name of God, take heed.
For never two such kingdoms did contend
Without much fall of blood, whose guiltless drops
Are every one a woe, a sore complaint
'Gainst him whose wrongs gives edge unto the swords
That makes such waste in brief mortality.
Under this conjuration speak, my lord,
For we will hear, note, and believe in heart
That what you speak is in your conscience washed   20
As pure as sin with baptism.

CANTERBURY

Then hear me, gracious sovereign, and you peers,
That owe yourselves, your lives, and services
To this imperial throne. There is no bar
To make against your highness' claim to France
But this, which they produce from Pharamond:
'In terram Salicam mulieres ne succedant' –
'No woman shall succeed in Salic land';
Which Salic land the French unjustly gloze
To be the realm of France, and Pharamond
The founder of this law and female bar.
Yet their own authors faithfully affirm
That the land Salic is in Germany,
Between the floods of Sala and of Elbe;
Where Charles the Great, having subdued the Saxons,
There left behind and settled certain French,
Who, holding in disdain the German women
For some dishonest manners of their life,
Established then this law: to wit, no female
Should be inheritrix in Salic land;   40

12 following: Henry's lines here are repetitions of those that come before and after them. Alan Howard (Henry) learnt them, and indeed, at the outset, performed them. Later, with them in mind, he could stress the other lines in such a way as to make the repetition unnecessary.

Which Salic, as I said, 'twixt Elbe and Sala,
Is at this day in Germany called Meisen.
Then doth it well appear the Salic law
Was not devisèd for the realm of France;
Nor did the French possess the Salic land
Until four hundred one-and-twenty years
After defunction of King Pharamond,
Idly supposed the founder of this law,
Who died within the year of our redemption
Four hundred twenty-six; and Charles the Great
Subdued the Saxons, and did seat the French
Beyond the river Sala, in the year
Eight hundred five. Besides, their writers say,
King Pepin, which deposèd Childeric,
Did, as heir general, being descended
Of Blithild, which was daughter to King Clothair,
Make claim and title to the crown of France.
Hugh Capet also–who usurped the crown   50
Of Charles the Duke of Lorraine, sole heir male
Of the true line and stock of Charles the Great
To find his title with some shows of truth,
Though in pure truth it was corrupt and naught,
Conveyed himself as th'heir to th'Lady Lingare,
Daughter to Charles le Chauve who was the son
To Lewis the Emperor, and Lewis the son
Of Charles the Great. Also King Lewis the Ninth,
Who was sole heir to this usurper Capet,
Could not keep quiet in his conscience,   60

44 following: These lines were cut at a very late stage–and perhaps should not have been.

The speech itself is difficult. Erudite, involved, historically inaccurate, it may be intended as a political ploy with a comic denoument. In which case boring your audience is a valid technique.

On the other hand it may be a real attempt by the Archbishop to explain the problems of sucession.

If it is the former, pace is acceptable and these lines could be included. We focus then upon the technique of the speaker. If it is the latter, the speech becomes interminable. The lines should go.

I confess that Derek Smith (Canterbury) and I never quite made up our minds between the two methods. Having watched the play for eight months I now feel more drawn to the former interpretation. The lines could go back.

Wearing the crown of France, till satisfied
That fair Queen Isabel, his grandmother,
Was lineal of the Lady Ermengare,
Daughter to Charles the foresaid Duke of Lorraine;
By the which marriage the line of Charles the Great
Was re-united to the crown of France.
So that, as clear as is the summer's sun,
King Pepin's title, and Hugh Capet's claim,
King Lewis his satisfaction, all appear
To hold in right and title of the female;   70
So do the kings of France unto this day,
Howbeit they would hold up this Salic law
To bar your highness claiming from the female,
And rather choose to hide them in a net
Than amply to imbar their crooked titles
Usurped from you and your progenitors.

KING HENRY
May I with right and conscience make this claim?

CANTERBURY
The sin upon my head, dread sovereign!
For in the Book of Numbers is it writ,
When the man dies, let the inheritance   80
Descend unto the daughter. Gracious lord,

77 May I with right and conscience.... Alan Howard (Henry): It is interesting
that Henry chooses to ask this question *after* the Archbishop's long and
detailed explanation of his claim, and also, that the question goes
unanswered–the Archbishop dodges it. I think Henry probably does want
to go to war with France: he is probably mindful of his father's death-bed
advice for dealing with English trouble-makers 'Busy (their) minds with foreign
quarrels..'. Also he is aware of the dubious claim his father had to the crown.
A successful war with France would settle once and for all any lingering
questions about his own right of succession.
81–154 Gracious lord. Stand for your own.... Having successfully shifted
everybody away from proper contemplation of church problems (the bill
mentioned in Scene I) the Archbishop reveals what is in everybody's mind–the
desire to fight in France.
    It may be that this is what Henry wants also, though he is the only one
who sees war in terms of death and misery. Here the court join in the
clarion-calls to war instigated by the Archbishop. Their unity of intention
is more important than the details they express. Hence the cuts. And as
they achieve vocal unity, so it was expressed physically on the stage.
    Henry is isolated from a baying group.

Stand for your own, unwind your bloody flag,
Look back into your mighty ancestors.
Go, my dread lord, to your great-grandsire's tomb,
From whom you claim; invoke his warlike spirit,
And your great-uncle's, Edward the Black Prince.
Who on the French ground played a tragedy,
Making defeat on the full power of France,
Whiles his most mighty father on a hill
Stood smiling to behold his lion's whelp
Forage in blood of French nobility.
O noble English, that could entertain
With half their forces the full pride of France,
And let another half stand laughing by,
All out of work and cold for action!

ELY

Awake remembrance of these valiant dead,
And with your puissant arm renew their feats.
You are their heir, you sit upon their throne,
The blood and courage that renownèd them
Runs in your veins; and my thrice-puissant liege
Is in the very May-morn of his youth,
Ripe for exploits and mighty enterprises.

EXETER

Your brother kings and monarchs of the earth
Do all expect that you should rouse yourself,   90
As did the former lions of your blood.

WESTMORELAND

They know your grace hath cause and means and might—
So hath your highness. Never King of England
Had nobles richer and more loyal subjects,
Whose hearts have left their bodies here in England
And lie pavilioned in the fields of France.

84 Look back into your ancestors... Alan Howard (Henry): It is interesting
that in their efforts to persuade him to go to war, all the other characters
emphasize his great-grandfather, and his great-uncle, Edward, the Black
Prince; the 'former lions of your blood' as Exeter calls them later. I think
Henry feels his inheritance from them very strongly, and perhaps tries to
model himself upon them—another factor behind his decision to go to war.
For this reason I asked for the surcoat to Henry's war armour to be based
upon that of the Black Prince.

CANTERBURY
 O, let their bodies follow, my dear liege,
 With blood and sword and fire to win your right!
 In aid whereof we of the spirituality
 Will raise your highness such a mighty sum
 As never did the clergy at one time   100
 Bring in to any of your ancestors.

KING HENRY
 We must not only arm t'invade the French
 But lay down our proportions to defend
 Against the Scot, *who will make road upon us*
 With all advantages.

CANTERBURY
 They of those marches, gracious sovereign,
 Shall be a wall sufficient to defend
 Our island from the pilfering borderers.

KING HENRY
 We do not mean the coursing snatchers only,
 But fear the main intendment of the Scot,
 Who hath been still a giddy neighbour to us;
 For you shall read that my great-grandfather
 Never went with his forces into France
 But that the Scot on his unfurnished kingdom
 Came pouring, like the tide into a breach,
 With ample and brim fullness of his force,   110
 Galling the gleaned land with hot assays,
 Girding with grievous siege castles and towns;
 That England, being empty of defence,
 Hath shook and trembled at th'ill neighbourhood.

CANTERBURY
 She hath been then more feared than harmed, my
  liege;
 For hear her but exampled by herself
 When all her chivalry hath been in France,
 And she a mourning widow of her nobles,
 She hath herself not only well defended
 But taken and impounded as a stray
 The King of Scots, whom she did send to France
 To fill King Edward's fame with prisoner kings,
 And make her chronicle as rich with praise

As is the ooze and bottom of the sea
With sunken wrack and sumless treasuries.

CLARENCE

But there's a saying very old and true:
'If that you will France win,
Then with Scotland first begin.'

GLOUCESTER

For once the eagle England being in prey,
To her unguarded nest the weasel Scot   120
Comes sneaking, and so sucks her princely eggs,
Playing the mouse in absence of the cat.
To 'tame and havoc more than she can eat.

EXETER

It follows then the cat must stay at home;

116–122 There's a saying…These lines, in Shakespeare's text, are given to
Ely. We re-allocated them to Clarence and Gloucester, as we wished to
introduce Henry's two brothers at this point. The brothers were extremely
important throughout the production, although they still have comparatively
few lines. Henry has three brothers: Bedford (the John of Lancaster of Henry
IV Part II), Gloucester, and Clarence. They were all played by actors who
bore a physical resemblance to Henry (Alan Howard), so that, when seen
together, the feeling of a family of four sons was as strong as possible. In
Henry V the cast list names all three brothers, although only Bedford and
Gloucester speak. We decided to retain Gloucester, develop Clarence, and
lose Bedford from the play. The cold Octavian John of Lancaster of *Part
II* seemed emotionally (though not historically) out of place in *Henry V.*
On the other hand, Clarence was Hal's favourite brother (cf. Henry IV's
words to him in *Part II*, Act IV Scene IV, 'Thou hast a better place in
his affections/Than all thy brothers'), and we used him in the play as the
one who was physically closest to Henry, who helped him to dress for battle
etc.

123 following: The cuts in Exeter's speech were made because his words
pre-empt the Archbishop's that follow, which should have as much weight
as possible behind them, dramatically. The Archbishop's much-loved and
much-anthologised speech is the full mediaeval statement of paternal fascism.
Everyone has his place; his place does not change; his duty is to maintain
the *status quo*, maintain order–a pre-determined order. It is the belief of
Richard II, of the court of Henry IV, and therefore of everyone in Henry
V's court. It is yet another aspect of traditional 'kingship' that Henry himself
will re-examine. On stage, Henry remained isolated from the others
throughout the speech, listening detachedly to a hierarchic philosophy that
kills kings, maintains unjust wealth, and makes men like the Archbishop
advocate unthinking wars. By the end of the play he will have created a
'band of brothers'.

Yet that is but a crushed necessity,
Since we have locks to safeguard necessaries,
And pretty traps to catch the petty thieves.
While that the armèd hand doth fight abroad,
Th'advisèd head defends itself at home;
For government, though high, and low, and lower,
Put into parts, doth keep in one consent,
Congreeing in a full and natural close,
Like music.

CANTERBURY
True. Therefore doth heaven divide
The state of man in divers functions,
Setting endeavour in continual motion;
To which is fixèd as an aim or butt   130
Obedience; for so work the honey-bees,
Creatures that by a rule in nature teach
The act of order to a peopled kingdom.
They have a king, and officers of sorts,
Where some, like magistrates, correct at home;
Others, like merchants, venture trade abroad;
Others, like soldiers, armèd in their stings,
Make boot upon the summer's velvet buds;
Which pillage they with merry march bring home
To the tent-royal of their emperor;   140
Who, busied in his majesty, surveys
The singing masons building roofs of gold,
The civil citizens kneading up the honey,
The poor mechanic porters crowding in
Their heavy burdens at his narrow gate,
The sad-eyed justice, with his surly hum,
Delivering o'er to executors pale
The lazy yawning drone. *I this infer,*
That many things, having full reference
To one consent, may work contrariously,
As many arrows loosèd several ways
Come to one mark,
As many several ways meet in one town,
As many fresh streams meet in one salt sea,
As many lines close in the dial's centre;
So may a thousand actions, once afoot,

End in one purpose, and be all well borne
Without defeat. Therefore to France, my liege!
Divide your happy England into four;
Whereof take you one quarter into France,   150
And you withal shall make all Gallia shake.
If we, with thrice such powers left at home,
Cannot defend our own doors from the dog,
Let us be worried, and our nation lose
The name of hardiness and policy.

KING HENRY
Call in the messengers sent from the Dauphin.
          Exeunt some attendants
Now are we well resolved, and by God's help
And yours, the noble sinews of our power,
France being ours, we'll bend it to our awe,
Or break it all to pieces. *Or there we'll sit,*   160
Ruling in large and ample empery
O'er France and all her almost kingly dukedoms,
Or lay these bones in an unworthy urn,
Tombless, with no remembrance over them.
Either our history shall with full mouth
Speak freely of our acts, or else our grave,
Like Turkish mute, shall have a tongueless mouth,

---

160 following: This was a late cut. Again the point has been made. The lines re-inforce the naivety of Henry's grandiloquence and emphasise the conventionality of his thinking.

Throughout this scene Henry hovers between realisation of the need for change, and perception of how to effect it. What sort of King should he be? What sort of Kingdom does he want?

Sometimes therefore he will hint at the future, sometimes speak in accents of the past–as here.

Like everybody in the play–following the Chorus's first directions–he is learning how to play his part: rehearsing in fact.

161 The entrance of the Ambassador is also that of the first period costume on to the stage. He is dressed exactly according to period.

We chose to make him a bishop. Shakespeare merely indicates 'ambassador'. There was no set ambassadorial dress. We know from a study of the sources that the French embassy contained two churchmen.

It seemed not unreasonable to place the negotiations for opening hostilities in the hands of those who have most to do with it–the Archbishop of Canterbury and the ambassador. Both being churchmen, Shakespeare's first irony is maintained.

Not worshipped with a waxen epitaph.
   Enter the Ambassador of France
Now are we well prepared to know the pleasure
Of our fair cousin Dauphin; for we hear
Your greeting is from him, not from the King.

AMBASSADOR

May't please your majesty to give us leave
Freely to render what we have in charge,
Or shall we sparingly show you far off
The Dauphin's meaning and our embassy?

KING HENRY

We are no tyrant, but a Christian king,
Unto whose grace our passion is as subject
As is our wretches fettered in our prisons: 170
Therefore with frank and with uncurbèd plainness
Tell us the Dauphin's mind.

AMBASSADOR

Thus then, in few:
Your highness, lately sending into France,
Did claim some certain dukedoms, in the right
Of your great predecessor, King Edward the Third.
In answer of which claim, the Prince our master
Says that you savour too much of your youth,
And bids you be advised there's naught in France
That can be with a nimble galliard won;
You cannot revel into dukedoms there.   180
He therefore sends you, meeter for your spirit,
This tun of treasure; and, in lieu of this,
Desires you let the dukedoms that you claim
Hear no more of you. This the Dauphin speaks.

KING HENRY

What treasure, uncle?

186 following: Hal re-emerges suddenly from the persona of kingship that
Henry has been experimenting with–not totally successfully–earlier in the
scene. Whatever his disposition to heed his councillors–all urging war with
France–his own sense of humour cannot resist the youthful challenge of
the Dauphin; the lines ring with sudden zest. But Hal needs to prove what
he says: the others suspect that he will be a 'good' king, that he has transformed
himself–but they are still cautious: 'The courses of his youth promised it
not'. As a king, and, it must be remembered, to this group of people, as
a person, Henry is still an unknown quantity.

EXETER   Tennis-balls, my liege.

KING HENRY

We are glad the Dauphin is so pleasant with us.
His present, and your pains, we thank you for.
When we have matched our rackets to these balls,
We will in France, by God's grace, play a set
Shall strike his father's crown into the hazard.   190
Tell him he hath made a match with such a wrangler
That all the courts of France will be disturbed
With chases. And we understand him well,
How he comes o'er us with our wilder days,
Not measuring what use we made of them.
We never valued this poor seat of England,
And therefore, living hence, did give ourself
To barbarous licence, as 'tis ever common
That men are merriest when they are from home.
But tell the Dauphin I will keep my state,   200
Be like a king, and show my sail of greatness,
When I do rouse me in my throne of France.
For that I have laid by my majesty,
And plodded like a man for working-days;
But I will rise there with so full a glory
That I will dazzle all the eyes of France,
Yea, strike the Dauphin blind to look on us.
And tell the pleasant Prince this mock of his
Hath turned his balls to gun-stones, and his soul
Shall stand sore chargèd for the wasteful vengeance   210
That shall fly with them: for many a thousand widows
Shall this his mock mock out of their dear husbands;
Mock mothers from their sons, mock castles down;
And some are yet ungotten and unborn
That shall have cause to curse the Dauphin's scorn.
But this lies all within the will of God,

215 following: The cuts are made here to preserve the overall rhythm of the speech.

Again Henry is practising. Arguably the irony of appealing to God and his devious minister the Archbishop would be emphasised by the inclusion of these lines. On the other hand the chance comes again ten lines later. Henry surely knows now that one of the reasons why he is committed to war in France is to save the Church money.

To whom I do appeal, and in whose name,
Tell you the Dauphin, I am coming on,
To venge me as I may, and to put forth
My rightful hand in a well-hallowed cause.
So get you hence in peace; and tell the Dauphin
His jest will savour but of shallow wit
When thousands weep more than did laugh at it.
Convey them with safe conduct. Fare you well.
    Exit Ambassador

EXETER
This was a merry message.   220

KING HENRY
We hope to make the sender blush at it.
Therefore, my lords, omit no happy hour
That may give furtherance to our expedition;
For we have now no thought in us but France,
Save those to God, that run before our business.
Therefore let our proportions for these wars
Be soon collected, and all things thought upon
That may with reasonable swiftness add
More feathers to our wings; for, God before,
We'll chide this Dauphin at his father's door.
Therefore let every man now task his thought
That this fair action may on foot be brought.
    Exeunt

CHORUS
Now all the youth of England are on fire,
And silken dalliance in the wardrobe lies,
Now thrive the armourers, and honour's thought
Reigns solely in the breast of every man.
They sell the pasture now to buy the horse,
Following the mirror of all Christian kings
With wingèd heels, as English Mercuries.

7 **Chorus: As English Mercuries...** the Chorus, having called upon the imagination of the audience, now calls upon that of the designer. He signals and the full apparatus of proscenium theatre goes into action. Music plays, a giant heraldic canopy billows open over the stage, a huge cannon on its trailer is swept into position, the actors gather about it and begin dressing and arming for war. Where we break his speech he is addressed by Nym. The second half of his speech moves to the beginning of our Scene IV.

For now sits expectation in the air,
And fills a sword from hilts unto the point
With crowns imperial, crowns and coronets,   10
Promised to Harry and his followers.

Scene III

Enter Nym and Bardolph

NYM

I dare not fight, but I will wink and hold out mine
iron. It is a simple one, but what though? It will toast
cheese, and it will endure cold as another man's sword
will–and there's an end.

BARDOLPH

Well met, Corporal Nym.

NYM

Good morrow, Lieutenant Bardolph.

BARDOLPH

What, are Ancient Pistol and you friends yet?

NYM

For my part I care not. I say little; but when time
shall serve, there shall be smiles–but that shall be   10
as it may.

BARDOLPH

I will bestow a breakfast to make you friends, and
we'll be all three sworn brothers to France. Let it
be so, good Corporal Nym.

Scene III: The process of building the play has been going on for twenty
minutes. Costumes have appeared. Now the play itself starts to take over.
The Chorus, who has instigated the proceedings, should be shown to have
a lessening control over it. He is therefore addressed and interrupted by
Bardolph and Nym. They include him in their conversation. And as their
scene, ribald and music hall, is the exact opposite of the heroic sentiments
expressed by the Chorus he retreats from the unequal combat.

They are an apparent front cloth act, while apparently more serious
proceedings continue in the background where the English Soldiers are
putting on their armour for war.

It is a change of acting-style. Having heard the 'rhetoricks' we are now
confronted by the 'mechanicals'

NYM

> Faith I will live as long as I may, that's the certain
> of it; and when I cannot live any longer, I will do
> as I may. That is my rest, that is the rendezvous of
> it.

BARDOLPH

> It is certain, Corporal, that he is married to Nell
> Quickly, and certainly he did you wrong, for you were   20
> troth-plight to her.

NYM

> I cannot tell; things must be as they may. *Men may*
> *sleep, and they may have their throats about them at*
> *that time, and some say knives have edges; it must be*
> *as it may—though patience be a tired mare, yet she*
> *will plod—there must be conclusions—well, I cannot tell.*
>   *Enter Pistol and Hostess Quickly*

BARDOLPH

> Here comes Ancient Pistol and his wife. Good
> Corporal, be patient here.

NYM

> Now now, mine host Pistol?

PISTOL

> Base tike, call'st thou me host?
> Now by this hand I swear I scorn the term;
> Nor shall my Nell keep lodgers.

HOSTESS

> No, by my troth, not long; for we cannot lodge and
> board a dozen or fourteen gentlewomen that live   30
> honestly by the prick of their needles but it will be
> thought we keep a bawdy-house straight.
>   *Nym draws his sword*
> O well-a-day, Lady, if he be not drawn now! We shall
> see wilful adultery and murder committed.

BARDOLPH

> Good Lieutenant! Good Corporal! Offer nothing here.

NYM

> Pish!

23 Here comes Ancient Pistol and his wife… In our production Pistol and
Nell Quickly enter fresh from their wedding. Bardolph drinks their health,
and scatters confetti. It is an unlikely match.

PISTOL

Pish for thee, Iceland dog! thou prick-eared cur of
Iceland!

HOSTESS

Good Corporal Nym, show thy valour, and put up   40
your sword.

NYM

Will you shog off? I would have you 'solus'.

He sheathes his sword

PISTOL

'Solus', egregious dog? O viper vile!
The 'solus' in thy most mervailous face!
The 'solus' in thy teeth and in thy throat,
And in thy hateful lungs, yea, in thy maw, perdy!
And, which is worse, within thy nasty mouth!
I do retort the 'solus' in thy bowels,
For I can take, and Pistol's cock is up,
And flashing fire will follow.

NYM

I am not Barbason; you cannot conjure me. I have
an humour to knock you indifferently well. If you   50
grow foul with me, Pistol, I will scour you with my
rapier, as I may, in fair terms. *If you would walk off
I would prick your guts a little, in good terms, as I
may*, and that's the humour of it.

PISTOL

O braggart vile, and damnèd furious wight!
The grave doth gape, and doting death is near:
Therefore exhale!

They both draw

BARDOLPH

Hear me, hear me what I say! He that strikes the
first stroke, I'll run him up to the hilts, as I am a
soldier.

He draws

---

47 For I can take, and Pistol's cock is up... The company on stage, getting
changed, applaud with whistles and shouts Pistol's favourite sally. The element
of 'performance' is still very marked.

PISTOL

An oath of mickle might, and fury shall abate.   60
Pistol and Nym sheathe their swords
Give me thy fist, thy forefoot to me give;
Thy spirits are most tall.

NYM

I will cut thy throat one time or other, in fair terms,
that is the humour of it.

PISTOL

'Couple a gorge!'
That is the word. I thee defy again!
O hound of Crete, think'st thou my spouse to get?
No, to the spital go,
And from the powdering tub of infamy
Fetch forth the lazar kite of Cressid's kind,   70
Doll Tearsheet she by name, and her espouse.
I have, and I will hold, the quondam Quickly
For the only she; and – 'pauca', there's enough.
Go to!
Enter the Boy

BOY

Mine host Pistol, you must come to my master – and
you, Hostess: he is very sick, and would to bed. Good
Bardolph, put thy nose between his sheets, and do
the office of a warming-pan. Faith, he's very ill.

BARDOLPH

Away, you rogue!

HOSTESS

By my troth, *he'll yield the crow a pudding one of these*   80
days, the King has killed his heart. Good husband,
come home presently.
Exit with Boy

BARDOLPH

Come, shall I make you two friends? We must to
France together: why the devil should we keep knives
to cut one another's throats?

PISTOL

Let floods o'erswell, and fiends for food howl on!

NYM

You'll pay me the eight shillings I won of you at betting?

PISTOL

Base is the slave that pays!

NYM

That now I will have; that's the humour of it.   90

PISTOL

As manhood shall compound. Push home!

They draw

BARDOLPH

By this sword, he that makes the first thrust, I'll kill him! By this sword, I will.

PISTOL

Sword is an oath, and oaths must have their course.

He sheathes his sword

BARDOLPH

Corporal Nym, an thou wilt be friends, be friends: an thou wilt not, why then be enemies with me too. Prithee put up.

NYM

I shall have my eight shillings *I won of you at betting?*

PISTOL

A noble shalt thou have, and present pay.
And liquor likewise will I give to thee,
And friendship shall combine, and brotherhood.
I'll live by Nym, and Nym shall live by me.
Is not this just? For I shall sutler be
Unto the camp, and profits will accrue.
Give me thy hand.

Nym sheathes his sword

NYM

I shall have my noble?

PISTOL

In cash most justly paid.

92 By this sword... Bardolph, for all the red-nosed result of excess revelry, has a certain sturdy courage. He is a soldier. He is a corporal. The dissension before even the army embarks is tempered by his 'professional' peace-making.

NYM
Well then, that's the humour of't.
Enter Hostess
HOSTESS
As ever you came of women, come in quickly to Sir
John. Ah, poor heart! he is so shaked of a burning
quotidian tertian that it is most lamentable to behold. 100
Sweet men, come to him.
NYM
The King hath run bad humours on the knight, that's
the even of it.
PISTOL
Nym, thou hast spoke the right;
His heart is fracted and corroborate.
NYM
The King is a good king, but it must be as it may:
he passes some humours and careers.
PISTOL
Let us condole the knight; for, lambkins, we will live.
Exeunt
CHORUS
The French, advised by good intelligence
Of this most dreadful preparation,
Shake in their fear, and with pale policy
Seek to divert the English purposes.
O England! model to thy inward greatness,
Like little body with a mighty heart,
What mightst thou do, that honour would thee do,
Were all thy children kind and natural!
But see, thy fault France hath in thee found out,
A nest of hollow bosoms, which he fills   10

98 With Quickly's re-entrance, and the news of Falstaff, the tone of the
scene suddenly changes.
 Richard Moore (Pistol): "Nym, Pistol and Bardolph don't take their
quarrelling and brawling seriously. They all know full well that they will
never really fight, or damage each other – they just play a game of threatened
fights that is understood as such between them."
 Suddenly something real is happening; Falstaff, who has been the backbone
of this group may die. The reminder of mortality draws the swaggerers out
of caricature, and into the play.
 Shakespeare completes another step in his 'acting' story.

With treacherous crowns; and three corrupted men—
One, Richard Earl of Cambridge, and the second,
Henry Lord Scroop of Masham, and the third,
Sir Thomas Grey, knight, of Northumberland—
Have, for the gilt of France—O guilt indeed!—
Confirmed conspiracy with fearful France;
And by their hands this grace of kings must die,
If hell and treason hold their promises,
Ere he take ship for France, and in Southampton.
Linger your patience on, and we'll digest   20
Th'abuse of distance, force a play.
The sum is paid; the traitors are agreed;
The King is set from London; and the scene
Is now transported, gentles, to Southampton.
There is the playhouse now, there must you sit,
And thence to France shall we convey you safe
And bring you back, charming the narrow seas
To give you gentle pass; for, if we may,
We'll not offend one stomach with our play.
But till the King come forth, and not till then,   30
Unto Southampton do we shift our scene.

Scene IV

At Southampton. The three traitors are on stage.
Enter Exeter, Gloucester, Westmoreland and
Clarence

GLOUCESTER

Fore God, his grace is bold to trust these traitors.

EXETER

They shall be apprehended by and by.

WESTMORELAND

How smooth and even they do bear themselves!

Scene IV: The chorus is still talking of 'forcing a play'. We are still forced
to be aware that the evening is the joint responsibility of audience and actor.
We are still unable to relax into 'illusion'.

As if allegiance in their bosoms sat,
Crownèd with faith and constant loyalty.

CLARENCE

The King hath note of all that they intend,
By interception which they dream not of.

EXETER

Nay, but the man that was his bedfellow,
Whom he hath dulled and cloyed with gracious favours –
That he should, for a foreign purse, so sell
His sovereign's life to death and treachery!
    Sound trumpets. Enter the King and attendants

KING HENRY

Now sits the wind fair, and we will aboard.
My Lord of Cambridge, and my kind Lord of   10
    Masham,
And you, my gentle knight, give me your thoughts.
Think you not that the powers we bear with us
Will cut their passage through the force of France,
Doing the execution and the act
For which we have in head assembled them?

Accordingly, in our production the traitors are announced non-naturalistically. Picked out by follow spots as the chorus names them, they are figures rather than people. They wear black robes over their rehearsal clothes, gold pectoral crosses contrasting with the red cross of St. George emblazoned on the sweeping white cloaks of Henry's lords.

We are at Southampton. The music suggests a pier-side band. Farewell to Blighty.

The scene is very mobile. The staging grew out of improvisation and was never fixed.

Three men wish to murder Henry.

Four men (Westmoreland, Exeter, Gloucester, Clarence) wish to prevent that murder.

Neither side wishes to give away its intentions.

Henry alone can provide a solution.

He knows the situation, and the several intentions. The longer he can play the game (with his life as the ball) the more he will learn of his friends and enemies.

It is a harsh introduction to politics.

We play more of the text of this scene than is usual. Henry has much to learn. Still trying to play the expected role of king, he is now faced with the emotional shock of betrayal.

9 Henry enters costumed for war, but without his heraldic surcoat which will be the banner of war and mark his full acceptance of leadership.

SCROOP

No doubt, my liege, if each man do his best.

KING HENRY

We doubt not that, since we are well persuaded
We carry not a heart with us from hence
That grows not in a fair consent with ours,
Nor leave not one behind that doth not wish   20
Success and conquest to attend on us.

CAMBRIDGE

Never was monarch better feared and loved
Than is your majesty. *There's not, I think, a subject*
That sits in heart-grief and uneasiness
Under the sweet shade of your government.

GREY

True: those that were your father's enemies
Have steeped their galls in honey, and do serve you
With hearts create of duty and of zeal.

KING HENRY

We therefore have great cause of thankfulness,
And shall forget the office of our hand
Sooner than quittance of desert and merit
According to the weight and worthiness.

SCROOP

So service shall with steelèd sinews toil,
And labour shall refresh itself with hope,
To do your grace incessant services.

KING HENRY

We judge no less. Uncle of Exeter,   30
Enlarge the man committed yesterday
That railed against our person. We consider
It was excess of wine that set him on,
And on his more advice we pardon him.

SCROOP

That's mercy, but too much security.
Let him be punished, sovereign, lest example
Breed, by his sufferance, more of such a kind.

KING HENRY

O, let us yet be merciful.

CAMBRIDGE

So may your highness, and yet punish too.

GREY

    Sir,   40

    You show great mercy if you give him life

    After the taste of much correction.

KING HENRY

    Alas, your too much love and care of me

    Are heavy orisons 'gainst this poor wretch!

    If little faults, proceeding on distemper,

    Shall not be winked at, how shall we stretch our eye

    When capital crimes, chewed, swallowed, and digested,

    Appear before us? We'll yet enlarge that man,

    Though Cambridge, Scroop, and Grey, in their dear

        care

    And tender preservation of our person   50

    Would have him punished. And now to our French

        causes:

    Who are the late commissioners?

CAMBRIDGE

    I one, my lord.

    Your highness bade me ask for it today.

SCROOP

    So did you me, my liege.

GREY

    And I, my royal sovereign.

KING HENRY

    Then, Richard Earl of Cambridge, there is yours;

    There yours, Lord Scroop of Masham; and, sir knight,

    Grey of Northumberland, this same is yours.

    Read them, and know I know your worthiness.   60

    My Lord of Westmoreland, and uncle Exeter,

    We will aboard tonight. Why, how now, gentlemen?

43–51 Henry gives the traitors every chance to clear or implicate themselves.
He listens to lies and flattery.

    He even explores the possibility of mercy. By demanding their opinion
of a minor misdemeanour he qualifies with their own words the judgement
he will pass on them. Cambridge, Scroop and Grey condemn the soldier
who has insulted the king's name. As aristocrats they are bound to. Henry–the
previous Hal–is already aware that these hierarchic opinions must change,
be re-assessed. He pardons 'the poor wretch'. Whether the offence was real,
or invented by Henry, the result is the same. He reveals the failing of the
'old' order, the need for change.

What see you in those papers, that you lose
So much complexion? Look ye, how they change!
Their cheeks are paper.—Why, what read you there
That have so cowarded and chased your blood
Out of appearance?

CAMBRIDGE   I do confess my fault,
And do submit me to your highness' mercy.

GREY, SCROOP
To which we all appeal.

KING HENRY
The mercy that was quick in us but late   70
By your own counsel is suppressed and killed.

70–120 This is an immense speech, of terrible intensity. And yet it is about someone we have never met, nor will again; who has been introduced like a morality play villain, and is never given the chance to bring depth or detail to his characterisation. Presumably therefore Shakespeare has other intentions. It is not the treason that matters, but its effect upon Henry: it is not the traitor we are to examine, but Henry himself.

The king cannot be the simple warrior-patriot he is often described as, when he can express such personal hurt. His sensitivities to personal betrayal are as keen as his father's. His anger is frightening. His sense is not just of betrayed trust—but love.

One cannot help asking who in the previous plays could have had such an effect upon Hal. Only Falstaff: 'I'll be a traitor then when thou art king.'

This scene falls between the news of Falstaff's illness, and the story of his death. The juxtaposition seems hardly accidental.

70–120 Alan Howard (Henry): The extraordinary rage and hurt that Henry expresses here has been glimpsed before: his father shows similar tendencies, as far back as *Richard II*, when he sentences Bushey, Bagot and Green to their deaths. In *Parts I* and *II* Hal's reaction to disloyalty is always fierce—witness his coldness and disappointment with Poins (who cynically expects Hal to be disloyal to his sick father), after he receives Falstaff's letter and learns that Poins has been trying to engineer a marriage between himself, and Poins' sister, Nell; witness his cold break with Falstaff, long before 'I know you not, old man', at the Boar's Head tavern in *Part II*, when Falstaff tries to save his own skin at the expense of Doll Tearsheet, Bardolph, Mistress Quickly and his boy—by claiming that they are all 'of the wicked' and that he dispraised Hal to them for that reason. It is worth noting that all the qualities he lists as being Scroop's are precisely the qualities Falstaff lacked. 'Free from gross passion, or of mirth or anger' is very close to Hamlet's words—'Give me that man that is not passion's slave'. Henry is certainly not free himself from such passions: he has chosen a man who is to be his close companion, and the man betrays him. The effect, just as he is attempting to embark for war as a model king, is catastrophic.

You must not dare, for shame, to talk of mercy,
For your own reasons turn into your bosoms
As dogs upon their masters, worrying you.
See you, my Princes, and my noble peers,
These English monsters! My Lord of Cambridge here –
You know how apt our love was to accord
To furnish him with all appertinents
Belonging to his honour; and this man
Hath, for a few light crowns, lightly conspired,   80
And sworn unto the practices of France,
To kill us here in Hampton: to the which
This knight, no less for bounty bound to us
Than Cambridge is, hath likewise sworn. But O,
What shall I say to thee, Lord Scroop, thou cruel,
Ingrateful, savage, and inhuman creature?
Thou that didst bear the key of all my counsels,
That knew'st the very bottom of my soul,
That almost mightst have coined me into gold,
Wouldst thou have practised on me, for thy use?   90
May it be possible that foreign hire
Could out of thee extract one spark of evil
That might annoy my finger? 'Tis so strange
That, though the truth of it stands off as gross
As black and white, my eye will scarcely see it.
Treason and murder ever kept together,
As two yoke-devils sworn to either's purpose,
Working so grossly in a natural cause
That admiration did not whoop at them.
But thou, 'gainst all proportion, didst bring in
Wonder to wait on treason and on murder:
And whatsoever cunning fiend it was
That wrought upon thee so preposterously
Hath got the voice in hell for excellence.
All other devils that suggest by treasons
Do botch and bungle up damnation
With patches, colours, and with forms, being fetched
From glistering semblances of piety;
But he that tempered thee bade thee stand up,
Gave thee no instance why thou shouldst do treason,
Unless to dub thee with the name of traitor.

If that same demon that hath gulled thee thus
Should with his lion gait walk the whole world,   100
He might return to vasty Tartar back,
And tell the legions, 'I can never win
A soul so easy as that Englishman's.'
O, how hast thou with jealousy infected
The sweetness of affiance! Show men dutiful?
Why, so didst thou. Seem they grave and learned?
Why, so didst thou. Come they of noble family?
Why, so didst thou. Seem they religious?
Why, so didst thou. Or are they spare in diet,
Free from gross passion or of mirth or anger,   110
Constant in spirit, not swerving with the blood,
Garnished and decked in modest complement,
Not working with the eye without the ear,
And but in purgèd judgement trusting neither?
Such and so finely bolted didst thou seem:
And thus thy fall hath left a kind of blot
To mark the full-fraught man and best endued
With some suspicion. I will weep for thee;
For this revolt of thine, methinks, is like
Another fall of man. Their faults are open.
Arrest them to the answer of the law;
And God acquit them of their practices!   120

EXETER

I arrest thee of high treason, by the name of
Richard Earl of Cambridge.
I arrest thee of high treason, by the name of Henry
Lord Scroop of Masham.
I arrest thee of high treason, by the name of Thomas
Grey, knight, of Northumberland.

SCROOP

Our purposes God justly hath discovered,
And I repent my fault more than my death,
Which I beseech your highness to forgive,
Although my body pay the price of it.   130

CAMBRIDGE

For me, the gold of France did not seduce,
Although I did admit it as a motive
The sooner to effect what I intended.

But God be thankèd for prevention,
Which I in sufferance heartily will rejoice,
Beseeching God and you to pardon me.

GREY

Never did faithful subject more rejoice
At the discovery of most dangerous treason
Than I do at this hour joy o'er myself,
Prevented from a damnèd enterprise.
My fault, but not my body, pardon, sovereign.

KING HENRY

God quit you in His mercy! Hear your sentence.
You have conspired against our royal person,
Joined with an enemy proclaimed, and from his
    coffers   140
Received the golden earnest of our death,
Wherein you would have sold your King to slaughter,
His princes and his peers to servitude,
His subjects to oppression and contempt,
And his whole kingdom into desolation.
Touching our person seek we no revenge,
But we our kingdom's safety must so tender,
Whose ruin you have sought, that to her laws
We do deliver you. Get you therefore hence,
Poor miserable wretches, to your death;   150
The taste whereof God of His mercy give
You patience to endure, and true repentance
Of all your dear offences. Bear them hence.
    Exeunt Cambridge, Scroop, and Grey, guarded
Now, lords, for France; the enterprise whereof
Shall be to you, as us, like glorious.
We doubt not of a fair and lucky war,

154–165 The traitors are formally condemned. But it is unthinkable that a man who has gone through the previous holocaust of emotions should now be cheerfully contemplating war.

In our production, Henry tries to pull himself together, but the omens are hardly auspicious.

Only his brothers, convinced and simpler in their responses, silently offer his sword and tabard and push him towards commitment.

Continued on next page.

Since God so graciously hath brought to light
This dangerous treason lurking in our way
To hinder our beginnings. We doubt not now
But every rub is smoothèd on our way.   160
Then forth, dear countrymen! Let us deliver
Our puissance into the hand of God,
Putting it straight in expedition.
Cheerly to sea! The signs of war advance!
No King of England if not King of France!
    Exeunt.

Scene V

*As Henry makes a triumphal exit, the shabby
figures of Pistol, The Hostess, Nym, Bardolph and
the Boy enter, the men kitted out for war.*

HOSTESS
Prithee, honey-sweet husband, let me bring thee to
Staines.

Footnote continued from previous page.

And at last Henry does commit himself. Fully costumed, he leaps 'heroically'
upon the cart carrying the cannon, and 'heroically' leads his army away.
    'Cheerly to sea! The signs of war advance!
    No King of England if not King of France!'
At this point Guy Woolfenden introduced a marching song—Deo
Gracias—which was to become the theme tune of the play. Here it was used
triumphantly, the exterior pageant of war, covering the interior anguish and
unease we have just witnessed.
    The heraldry of this sequence is undercut by the sombre reality of Sc. V.
154–165 Alan Howard (Henry): There is no way, after the preceding speech,
that the 'Now lords..!' can be calm and sanguine. I discovered that in rehearsal:
the emotional force of the previous speech has to carry on, and affect the
second. And the second speech is not so complacent as it appears at first
sight: the repetitions of the word 'doubt', the strange phrase 'fair and *lucky*
war' (why should he need luck if everything is safely under control?), the
slight bitterness detectable in the words 'Since God so graciously hath brought
to light', the sudden glibness of the final couplet. All seem to me indications
that Henry is considerably shaken at this point, as he must be, unless the
previous speech is an aberration of Shakespeare's, or a piece of manufactured
cynicism on Henry's part (which it clearly isn't). Henry's confidence in his
chosen role seems to me to have been badly thrown; he is uncertain which
way God is going to throw the dice. He pulls himself together by the end
of the speech, and manages a clarion-call with 'Cheerly to sea! the signs
of war advance...'

PISTOL

No, for my manly heart doth earn.
Bardolph, be blithe! Nym, rouse thy vaunting veins!
Boy, bristle thy courage up! For Falstaff, he is dead,
And we must earn therefor.

BARDOLPH

Would I were with him, wheresome'er he is, either
in heaven or in hell!

HOSTESS

Nay, sure, he's not in hell: he's in Arthur's bosom,
if ever man went to Arthur's bosom. 'A made a finer
end, and went away an it had been any christom child;
'a parted e'en just between twelve and one, e'en at   10
the turning o'th'tide; for after I saw him fumble with
the sheets, and play with flowers, and smile upon his
fingers' ends, I knew there was but one way; for his
nose was as sharp as a pen, and 'a babbled of green
fields. 'How now, Sir John?' quoth I, 'What, man, be
o'good cheer!' So 'a cried out, 'God, God, God!' three
or four times. Now I, to comfort him, bid him 'a should
not think of God – I hoped there was no need to trouble
himself with any such thoughts yet. So 'a bade me
lay more clothes on his feet; I put my hand into the   20
bed, and felt them, and they were as cold as any stone;
then I felt to his knees, and so up'ard and up'ard,
and all was as cold as any stone.

BARDOLPH

They say he cried out of sack.

HOSTESS

Ay, that 'a did.

NYM

And of women.

HOSTESS

Nay, that 'a did not.

16 and 18 In Shakespeare's text Nym speaks the first line–'They say he
cried out of sack', and Bardolph speaks the second line–'And of women.'
In our production they were reversed.

Tim Wylton (Bardolph) felt that his character was more interested in drink.
Philip Dunbar (Nym) felt that his character worried about women. The
Director felt accommodating.

BOY

Yes, that 'a did, and said they were devils incarnate.

HOSTESS

'A could never abide carnation, 'twas a colour he never liked.

BOY

'A said once, the devil would have him about women. 30

HOSTESS

'A did in some sort, indeed, handle women; but then he was rheumatic, and talked of the Whore of Babylon.

BOY

Do you not remember, 'a saw a flea stick upon Bardolph's nose, and 'a said it was a black soul burning in hell?

BARDOLPH

Well, the fuel is gone that maintained that fire–that's all the riches I got in his service.

NYM

Shall we shog? The King will be gone from Southampton.

PISTOL

Come, let's away. My love, give me thy lips. 40
Look to my chattels and my movables.
Let senses rule. The word is 'Pitch and pay!'
Trust none;
For oaths are straws, men's faiths are wafer-cakes,
And Holdfast is the only dog, my duck.
Therefore, Caveto be thy counseller.
Go, clear thy crystals. Yoke-fellows in arms,
Let us to France, like horse-leeches, my boys,
To suck, to suck, the very blood to suck!

BOY

And that's but unwholesome food, they say. 50

PISTOL

Touch her soft mouth, and march.

BARDOLPH

Farewell, Hostess.
            He kisses her

NYM

I cannot kiss, that is the humour of it; but adieu.

PISTOL
Let housewifery appear. Keep close, I thee command.
HOSTESS
Farewell! Adieu!
Exeunt

Scene VI

*The French court. Enter the French King, the
Dauphin, the Constable and Montjoy*
FRENCH KING
Thus comes the English with full power upon us,
And more than carefully it us concerns
To answer royally in our defences.
Therefore the Dukes of Berri and Britaine,
Of Brabant and of Orleans, shall make forth,
And you, Prince Dauphin, with all swift dispatch,
To line and new repair our towns of war
With men of courage and with means defendant;
For England his approaches makes as fierce
As waters to the sucking of a gulf.   10
It fits us then to be as provident
As fear may teach us, out of late examples

55 Pistol, Nym, Bardolph and the Boy go off to war: Richard Moore (Pistol)
and Philip Dunbar (Nym): "We go off right at the back of the stage in
a thin straggly line, with tattered clothes, beaten-up equipment. And the
first words the French king says are 'Thus comes the English with full power
upon us.' The contrast is extraordinary, and the juxtaposition of the two
scenes so brilliant. We are part of that 'full force'–three aging men, marching
off, with the Boy beating a drum."
Scene VI: Up to this point, apart from the French Ambassador in Scene
II, the costuming has been largely modern, the costumes drawing inspiration
from both World Wars.
    With the appearance of the French a specific fifteenth-century element
is added. Their colours are blue, grey, gold. They are not going to war.
Their entrance is stately, to harp and flute. They are obsolete. The stillness
of the stageing, the follow spots, the echoing hall, suggest an etiquette-bound
remnant of the age of chivalry, the age of Richard II.
    Theatrically, period costume is an outmoded convention. Used here it helps
to accentuate the fact that the French are frozen in an era that has already
passed.

Left by the fatal and neglected English
Upon our fields.
DAUPHIN   My most redoubted father,
It is most meet we arm us 'gainst the foe;
For peace itself should not so dull a kingdom,
Though war nor no known quarrel were in question,
But that defences, musters, preparations,
Should be maintained, assembled, and collected,
As were a war in expectation.   20
Therefore, I say, 'tis meet we all go forth
To view the sick and feeble parts of France:
And let us do it with no show of fear—
No, with no more than if we heard that England
Were busied with a Whitsun morris-dance;
For, my good liege, she is so idly kinged,
Her sceptre so fantastically borne
By a vain, giddy, shallow, humorous youth,
That fear attends her not.
CONSTABLE   O, peace, Prince Dauphin!
You are too much mistaken in this King.   30
Question your grace the late ambassadors,
With what great state he heard their embassy,
How well supplied with noble counsellors,
How modest in exception, and withal
How terrible in constant resolution,
And you shall find his vanities forespent
Were but the outside of the Roman Brutus,
Covering discretion with a coat of folly;
As gardeners do with ordure hide those roots
That shall first spring and be most delicate.   40
DAUPHIN
Well, 'tis not so, my Lord High Constable;
But though we think it so, it is no matter.
In cases of defence, 'tis best to weigh
The enemy more mighty than he seems.
So the proportions of defence are filled;

15–29 The Dauphin is like Hal or Hotspur in *Henry IV Part I*, irritated
   by the constrictions of etiquette, challenging the older men.
   The French in general don't want war, as their answers to the Dauphin
make clear. The Dauphin does.

Which of a weak and niggardly projection
Doth like a miser spoil his coat with scanting
A little cloth.

FRENCH KING

Think we King Harry strong;
And, Princes, look you strongly arm to meet him.
The kindred of him hath been fleshed upon us,
And he is bred out of that bloody strain
That haunted us in our familiar paths.
Witness our too much memorable shame   50
When Crécy battle fatally was struck,
And all our princes captived by the hand
Of that black name, Edward, Black Prince of Wales;
Whiles that his mountain sire, on mountain standing,
Up in the air, crowned with the golden sun,
Saw his heroical seed, and smiled to see him,
Mangle the work of nature, and deface
The patterns that by God and by French fathers
Had twenty years been made. This is a stem
Of that victorious stock; and let us fear   60
The native mightiness and fate of him.

MONTJOY

Ambassadors from Harry King of England
Do crave admittance to your majesty.

FRENCH KING

We'll give them present audience. Go and bring them.
You see this chase is hotly followed, friends.

DAUPHIN

Turn head, and stop pursuit, for coward dogs
Most spend their mouths when what they seem to
threaten
Runs far before them. Good my sovereign,
Take up the English short, and let them know
Of what a monarchy you are the head.   70
Self-love, my liege, is not so vile a sin
As self-neglecting.

62–63 Oliver Ford-Davies played both the Ambassador and Montjoy the
Herald. A similar function, if different costume.
    Here he is introduced, and given the lines of an anonymous messenger.
Throughout the scene he notes the King's speeches; he announces the English.

H.V.—K

Enter Exeter, with Clarence and Gloucester

FRENCH KING   From our brother of England?

EXETER
From him; and thus he greets your majesty:
He wills you, in the name of God Almighty,
That you divest yourself, and lay apart
The borrowed glories that by gift of heaven,
By law of nature and of nations, 'longs
To him and to his heirs–namely, the crown,
And all wide-stretchèd honours that pertain
By custom and the ordinance of times   80
Unto the crown of France. That you may know
'Tis no sinister nor no awkward claim
Picked from the worm-holes of long-vanished days,
Nor from the dust of old oblivion raked,
He sends you this most memorable line,
In every branch truly demonstrative,
Willing you overlook this pedigree;
And when you find him evenly derived
From his most famed of famous ancestors,
Edward the Third, he bids you then resign   90
Your crown and kingdom, indirectly held
From him, the native and true challenger.

FRENCH KING
Or else what follows?

EXETER
Bloody constraint; for if you hide the crown
Even in your hearts, there will he rake for it.
Therefore in fierce tempest is he coming,
In thunder and in earthquake, like a Jove,
That, if requiring fail, he will compel;
And bids you, in the bowels of the Lord,
Deliver up the crown, and to take mercy   100
On the poor souls for whom this hungry war
Opens his vasty jaws; and on your head
Turning the widows' tears, the orphans' cries,
The dead men's blood, the privèd maidens' groans,
For husbands, fathers, and betrothèd lovers
That shall be swallowed in this controversy.
This is his claim, his threatening, and my message–

Unless the Dauphin be in presence here,
To whom expressly I bring greeting too.

FRENCH KING

For us, we will consider of this further.
Tomorrow shall you bear our full intent
Back to our brother of England.

DAUPHIN   For the Dauphin,
I stand here for him. What to him from England?   110

EXETER

Scorn and defiance, slight regard, contempt,
And anything that may not misbecome
The mighty sender, doth he prize you at.
Thus says my King: an if your father's highness
Do not, in grant of all demands at large,
Sweeten the bitter mock you sent his majesty,
He'll call you to so hot an answer of it
That caves and womby vaultages of France
Shall chide your trespass, and return your mock
In second accent of his ordinance.   120

DAUPHIN

Say, if my father render fair return,
It is against my will, for I desire
Nothing but odds with England. To that end,
As matching to his youth and vanity,
I did present him with the Paris balls.

EXETER

He'll make your Paris Louvre shake for it,
Were it the mistress court of mighty Europe:
And, be assured, you'll find a difference,

116 Sweeten the bitter mock… On this line both the Dauphin and the French King reacted—the Dauphin trying to stop Exeter saying anything further, because he has 'blown the gaff,' the French King surprised and angered.

Geoffrey Hutchings (Dauphin): The Dauphin clearly wants war passionately—'I desire nothing but odds with England'—and I felt that it was very possible that he had sent the tennis balls to Henry in order to provoke him, and without his father's knowledge. At that point, he tries to stop Exeter saying anything further but does not succeed. He wants to prove himself in war, and he seems to feel a bitter personal rivalry towards Henry. Both are sons of interfering fathers who continually tell them what to do. Henry's father is dead. The Dauphin's simply ignores all his son's wishes and arguments.

As we his subjects have in wonder found,
Between the promise of his greener days   130
And these he masters now. Now he weighs time
Even to the utmost grain; that you shall read
In your own losses, if he stay in France.

FRENCH KING
Tomorrow shall you know our mind at full.

EXETER
Dispatch us with all speed, lest that our King
Come here himself to question our delay,
For he is footed in this land already.

FRENCH KING
You shall be soon dispatched with fair conditions.
A night is but small breath and little pause
To answer matters of this consequence   140
> *Exeunt*
> *The stage darkens*; *drums roll*; *enter the Chorus*

CHORUS
Thus with imagined wing our swift scene flies
In motion of no less celerity
Than that of thought. Suppose that you have seen
The well-appointed King at Hampton pier
Embark his royalty, and his brave fleet
With silken streamers the young Phoebus fanning.
Play with your fancies, and in them behold
Upon the hempen tackle ship-boys climbing;
Hear the shrill whistle which doth order give
To sounds confused; behold the threaden sails,   10
Borne with th'invisible and creeping wind,
Draw the huge bottoms through the furrowed sea,
Breasting the lofty surge. O, do but think
You stand upon the rivage and behold
A city on th'inconstant billows dancing;
For so appears this fleet majestical,
Holding due course to Harfleur. Follow, follow!
Grapple your minds to sternage of this navy,
And leave your England, as dead midnight still,
Guarded with grandsires, babies, and old women,   20
Either past or not arrived to pith and puissance.
For who is he whose chin is but enriched

With one appearing hair that will not follow
These culled and choice-drawn cavaliers to France?
Work, work your thoughts, and therein see a siege:
Behold the ordnance on their carriages,
With fatal mouths gaping on girded Harfleur.
Suppose th'ambassador from the French comes back;
Tells Harry that the King doth offer him
Katherine his daughter, and with her, to dowry,   30
Some petty and unprofitable dukedoms.
The offer likes not; and the nimble gunner
With linstock now the devilish cannon touches,
And down goes all before them. Still be kind,
And eke out our performance with your mind.

Scene VII

*Harfleur. The English soldiers come crashing over
the breach, some falling to the ground, others
clinging to the scaling ladders. Henry comes over
the breach last*

KING HENRY
Once more unto the breach, dear friends, once more,
Or close the wall up with our English dead!
In peace there's nothing so becomes a man
As modest stillness and humility:
But when the blast of war blows in our ears,
Then imitate the action of the tiger;
Stiffen the sinews, conjure up the blood,
Disguise fair nature with hard-favoured rage;

24 **These culled and choice-drawn cavaliers**...On this line a thunder of timpani
heralds the lifting of a ramp, set in the stage floor, which–at a gradient
of 1 in 1-becomes the 'breach'. Four follow spots snap on, and focus the
Chorus. He continues.

At the end of the speech the light changes, battle tapes and musicians
play, and the actors playing the English swarm over the breach, down scaling
ladders and ropes.

It has taken us seven scenes in this so-called patriotic war play for the
English and the French to engage in battle. An hour of stage time. Battle
is finally joined, and the English are in retreat!

Then lend the eye a terrible aspect;
Let it pry through the portage of the head   10
Like the brass cannon; let the brow o'erwhelm it
As fearfully as does a gallèd rock
O'erhang and jutty his confounded base,
Swilled with the wild and wasteful ocean.
Now set the teeth, and stretch the nostril wide,
Hold hard the breath, and bend up every spirit
To his full height! On, on, you noblest English,
Whose blood is fet from fathers of war-proof!–
Fathers that, like so many Alexanders,
Have in these parts from morn till even fought,   20
And sheathed their swords for lack of argument.
Dishonour not your mothers; now attest
That those whom you called fathers did beget you!
Be copy now to men of grosser blood,
And teach them how to war. And you, good yeomen,
Whose limbs were made in England, show us here
The mettle of your pasture; let us swear
That you are worth your breeding–which I doubt
not;
For there is none of you so mean and base
That hath not noble lustre in your eyes.   30

Scene VII 1–34 Even in this speech Shakespeare still maintains his theatrical
metaphor.

Henry explains how to 'act' courage. 'Imitate', 'conjure', 'disguise'. He
describes the externals of performance.

And he still maintains the accepted distinction between lords and commons.
The former will instruct the latter.

By the time he reaches St Crispin's Day the acting will have become
'interior'–'all things are ready if our minds be so', and hierarchy will have
become 'brotherhood.'

1–34 Alan Howard (Henry): At moments of extreme physical test, Hal/Henry
seems to be able to draw on huge reserves of spirit and energy–he has
done so at the battle of Shrewsbury against Douglas and Hotspur, and he
does so again here. Playing the speech full tilt is like trying to run the
440 yards uphill in an opposing wind. It is an amazing performance, an
audition for himself in front of his men that must pay off: their backs are
literally to the wall. That he uses so many 'acting' words, as Terry Hands
notes, is interesting. So is the fact that he uses ancestors like talismans–if
memories and myths of his own family can charge him, perhaps thought
of their own fathers as 'Alexanders' can similarly charge his followers.

I see you stand like greyhounds in the slips,
Straining upon the start. The game's afoot!
Follow your spirit, and upon this charge
Cry, 'God for Harry, England and Saint George!'
Exeunt

Scene VIII

As the soldiers pour back over the breach Nym,
Bardolph, Pistol and the Boy remain behind.

BARDOLPH

On, on, on, on, on! To the breach, to the breach!

NYM

Pray thee, Corporal, stay–the knocks are too hot,
and, for mine own part, I have not a case of lives.
The humour of it is too hot, that is the very plainsong
of it.

PISTOL

The plainsong is most just; for humours do abound.
Knocks go and come; God's vassals drop and die;
    And sword and shield,
    In bloody field,
Doth win immortal fame.   10

BOY

Would I were in an alehouse in London! I would
give all my fame for a pot of ale, and safety.

PISTOL

And I
    If wishes would prevail with me,
    My purpose should not fail with me,
      But thither would I hie.

BOY

    As duly,
    But not as truly,
As bird doth sing on bough.

Scene VIII: At the end of Henry's speech the army pours back over the
wall, music and battle-sound urging them on.
  Bardolph, Nym, Pistol and the Boy do not follow.
  Not everybody is convinced. Not everybody is heroic.
  They crouch at the foot of the wall.
  They sing.

Enter Fluellen

FLUELLEN

Up to the breach, you dogs! Avaunt, you cullions! 20

He drives them forward

PISTOL

Be merciful, great Duke, to men of mould!
Abate thy rage, *abate thy manly rage*,
Abate thy rage, great Duke!
Good bawcock, bate thy rage! Use lenity, sweet chuck!

NYM

These be good humours! Your honour wins bad
humours.

Exeunt all but the Boy

BOY

As young as I am, I have observed these three swashers.
I am boy to them all three, but all they three, though
they would serve me, could not be man to me; for
indeed three such antics do not amount to a man.
For Bardolph, he is white-livered and red-faced; by 30
the means whereof 'a faces it out, but fights not. For
Pistol, he hath a killing tongue, and a quiet sword;
by the means whereof 'a breaks words, and keeps
whole weapons. For Nym, he hath heard that men
of few words are the best men; and therefore he scorns
to say his prayers, lest 'a should be thought a coward;
but his few bad words are matched with as few good
deeds, for 'a never broke any man's head but his own,
and that was against a post, when he was drunk. They
will steal anything, and call it purchase. Bardolph stole 40
a lute-case, bore it twelve leagues, and sold it for three
half-pence. Nym and Bardolph are sworn brothers
in filching, and in Calais they stole a fire-shovel. *I
knew by that piece of service the men would carry coals.*
They would have me as familiar with men's pockets
as their gloves or their handkerchers: which makes
much against my manhood, if I should take from
another's pocket to put into mine; for it is plain
pocketing up of wrongs. I must leave them, and seek
some better service. Their villainy goes against my 50
weak stomach, and therefore I must cast it up.

Exit
Enter Fluellen, Gower following

GOWER

Captain Fluellen, you must come presently to the mines. The Duke of Gloucester would speak with you.

FLUELLEN

To the mines? Tell you the Duke, it is not so good to come to the mines, for, look you, the mines is not according to the disciplines of the war. The concavities of it is not sufficient; for, look you, th'athversary, you may discuss unto the Duke, look you, is digt himself four yard under the countermines. By Cheshu, I think 'a will plow up all, if there is not better directions.   60

GOWER

The Duke of Gloucester, to whom the order of the

---

52 following: The four captains' scene. At this stage of the play the English army is disunited.

Shakespeare accentuates Henry's problem by introducing four captains (centurians of the Roman army, sergeant-majors of ours). They are responsible men, each from a different country. Clearly Shakespeare both mocks and respects their individual patriotism. They are real, but funny. Eccentrics all.

In rehearsal the actors added to Shakespeare's indications those elements of contemporary attitude which still (sometimes affectionately) define our island peoples.

Barrie Rutter emphasised the aggression, Catholicism, and delight in carnage of Macmorris, the Irish captain–in charge of explosives. Ken Stott (a Scotsman) pointed out the northern addiction to whisky of Jamy the Scots captain of infantry. Trevor Peacock brought to the fiery Welshman Fluellen, the pedantic bookmanship of the valleys and Derek Smith the phlegmatic English captain chewed sweets like Shaw's 'chocolate soldier'.

The comedy nonetheless is in their language. They simply can't understand one another.

Insults are given unintentionally, angers aroused through misunderstanding.

'Gentlemen you will mistake one another' says Gower, as Macmorris tries to cut off Fluellen's head. Apart from this being a classic English understatement, they have done nothing else.

It is a continuing theme of the Henry plays. This misunderstanding. This need to learn each other's language. Here Shakespeare shows that regional differences can be as insuperable as national ones. Henry has to unite his own country before he can win another. As a metaphor the war provides excuse for bringing all the disparate elements together. But they are still united by discipline, not understanding.

siege is given, is altogether directed by an Irishman,
a very valiant gentleman, i'faith.

FLUELLEN

It is Captain Macmorris, is it not?

GOWER

I think it be.

FLUELLEN

By Cheshu, he is an ass, as in the world; I will verify
as much in his beard. He has no more directions in
the true disciplines of the wars, look you, of the Roman
disciplines, than is a puppy-dog.

Enter Captain Macmorris and Captain
Jamy–Macmorris from under the stage, as if from
the mines.

GOWER

Here comes the Scots captain.   70

FLUELLEN

Captain Jamy is a marvellous falorous gentleman, that
is certain, and of great expedition and knowledge in
th'aunchient wars, upon my particular knowledge of
his directions. By Cheshu, he will maintain his
argument as well as any military man in the world,
in the disciplines of the pristine wars of the Romans.

JAMY

I say gud-day, Captain Fluellen.

FLUELLEN

Good-e'en to your worship, good Captain James.

GOWER

How now, Captain Macmorris, have you quit the
mines? Have the pioneers given o'er?   80

MACMORRIS

By Chrish, la, 'tish ill done! The work ish give over,
the trompet sound the retreat. By my hand I swear,
and my father's soul, the work ish ill done: it ish
give over. I would have blowed up the town, so Chrish
save me, sweet lord la, in an hour. O, 'tish ill done,
'tish ill done–by my hand, 'tish ill done!

FLUELLEN

Captain Macmorris, I beseech you now, will you
voutsafe me, look you, a few disputations with you,

as partly touching or concerning the disciples of the
war, the Roman wars, in the way of argument, look   90
you, and friendly communication?—partly to satisfy
my opinion, and partly for the satisfaction, look you,
of my mind—as touching the direction of the military
discipline, that is the point.

JAMY

It sall be vary gud, gud feith, gud captens bath, and
I shall quit you with gud leve, as I may pick occasion:
that sall I, marry.

MACMORRIS

This is no time to discourse, so Chrish save me! The
day is hot, and the weather, and the wars, and the
King, and the Dukes—it is no time to discourse, the   100
town is beseeched, and the trumpet call is to the breach,
and we talk, and, be Chrish, do nothing; 'tis shame
for us all: so God sa' me, 'tis shame to stand still,
it is shame, by my hand—and there is throats to be
cut, and works to be done, and there ish nothing done,
so Chrish sa' me, la!

JAMY

By the mess, ere theise eyes of mine take themselves
to slomber, ay'll de gud service, or ay'll lig i'th'grund
for it, ay, or go to death! And ay'll pay't as valorously
as I may, that sall I surely do, that is the breff and   110
the long. *Marry, I wad full fain hear some question
'tween you tway.*

FLUELLEN

Captain Macmorris, I think, look you, under your
correction, there is not many of your nation—

MACMORRIS

Of my nation? What ish my nation? Ish a villain,
and a bastard, and a knave, and a rascal. What ish
my nation? Who talks of my nation?

FLUELLEN

Look you, if you take the matter otherwise than is
meant, Captain Macmorris, peradventure I shall think
you do not use me with that affability as in discretion
you ought to use me, look you, being as good a man   120

as yourself, both in the disciplines of war, and in the derivation of my birth, and in other particularities.

MACMORRIS
I do not know you so good a man as myself. So Chrish save me, I will cut off your head.

GOWER
Gentlemen both, you will mistake each other.

JAMY
Ah, that's a foul fault!
A parley is sounded

GOWER
The town sounds a parley.

FLUELLEN
Captain Macmorris, when there is more better opportunity to be required, look you, I will be so bold as to tell you, I know the disciplines of war; and there is an end.   130

Scene IX

Harfleur. Henry, Exeter and the English soldiers enter. Henry moves down-stage to address the Governor of the city

KING HENRY
How yet resolves the Governor of the town?
This is the latest parle we will admit:
Therefore to our best mercy give yourselves,
Or, like to men proud of destruction,
Defy us to our worst; for, as I am a soldier,
A name that in my thoughts becomes me best,
If I begin the battery once again,
I will not leave the half-achieved Harfleur
Till in her ashes she lie burièd.
The gates of mercy shall be all shut up,   10

1–43 Henry in full war panoply faces the audience, his army behind him. The Governor of Harfleur speaks from the upper circle. The impact of Henry's lines is directly received by the audience. They become Harfleur.
  Alan Howard (Henry): The speech to the Governor is made in front of his soldiers, and much depends upon it. Like the speech at the breach

And the fleshed soldier, rough and hard of heart,
In liberty of bloody hand shall range
With conscience wide as hell, mowing like grass
Your fresh fair virgins, and your flowering infants.
What is it then to me, if impious war,
Arrayed in flames, like to the prince of fiends,
Do, with his smirched complexion, all fell feats
Enlinked to waste and desolation?
What is't to me, when you yourselves are cause,
If your pure maidens fall into the hand
Of hot and forcing violation?
What rein can hold licentious wickedness
When down the hill he holds his fierce career?
We may as bootless spend our vain command
Upon th'enragèd soldiers in their spoil
As send precepts to the leviathan
To come ashore. Therefore, you men of Harfleur,
Take pity of your town and of your people
Whiles yet my soldiers are in my command,
Whiles yet the cool and temperate wind of grace   30
O'erblows the filthy and contagious clouds
Of heady murder, spoil, and villainy.
If not, why, in a moment look to see
The blind and bloody soldier with foul hand
Defile the locks of your shrill-shrieking daughters;
Your fathers taken by the silver beards,
And their most reverend heads dashed to the walls;

it is another test for Henry. The speech must surely be read in the light
of his words immediately after it, once the Governor has surrendered: the
winter is coming on, his soldiers are sick (they were, with dysentery), and
he instructs them to use mercy. This is in complete conflict with the savagery
of the images which he uses to the Governor, whom he *has* to persuade
to surrender. Henry is clearly obsessed with the word 'soldier' and its
implications. He uses the word five times in the speech; he begins by saying
that 'soldier' is a term that 'in my thoughts becomes me best'–as if it were
the role he had chosen as best to play–and then goes on to paint a picture
of soldiering which is as cruel, and as evil, as he can make it. Throughout,
soldiers are linked with images of hell. He needs the power of rhetoric at
this moment; it comes to him. When the Governor surrenders, he is relieved
and, I think, deeply moved. In the speech, his imagination explores the
possibilities of destruction; his first action after the surrender, when rape
and plunder and murder could still be possible, is to forbid it.

Your naked infants spitted upon pikes,
Whiles the mad mothers with their howls confused
Do break the clouds, as did the wives of Jewry   40
At Herod's bloody-hunting slaughtermen.
What say you? Will you yield, and this avoid?
Or, guilty in defence, be thus destroyed?

GOVERNOR
Our expectation hath this day an end.
The Dauphin, whom of succours we entreated,
Returns us that his powers are yet not ready
To raise so great a siege. Therefore, great King,
We yield our town and lives to thy soft mercy.
Enter our gates, dispose of us and ours,
For we no longer are defensible.   50

KING HENRY
Open your gates.
                    Come, uncle Exeter,
Go you and enter Harfleur; there remain,
And fortify it strongly 'gainst the French.
Use mercy to them all. For us, dear uncle,
The winter coming on, and sickness growing
Upon our soldiers, we will retire to Calais.
Tonight in Harfleur will we be your guest;
Tomorrow for the march are we addressed.
        Exit the army

51–59 Henry has conquered Harfleur, but with great difficulty, after a
near-disastrous retreat. The conquering of Harfleur tends to make people
forget the sequence of events that comes between it and the Battle of Agincourt.
Immediately after the fall of Harfleur Henry makes the decision to return
to England–'we will retire to Calais'. His soldiers are sick and depleted;
his army can advance no further. Despite the victory at Harfleur, his campaign
has failed. There are no false heroics, no death-or-glory charges–just a quiet
acceptance of reality. Henry's desolation and loneliness are complete. He
has played all the right roles. But it still doesn't work.

Scene X

*Henry remains on stage, alone, as the breach slowly
lowers back into the floor of the stage. Behind
it is Katherine, the Princess of France. Henry
leaves as Alice enters*

KATHERINE
Alice, Alice!

ALICE
Madame?

KATHERINE
Alice, tu as été en Angleterre, et tu parles bien le
langage.

ALICE
Un peu, madame.

KATHERINE
Il faut que j'apprenne à parler.

ALICE
Oui madame.

KATHERINE
Bien. Je te prie, m'enseignez–Comment appelez-vous
la main en anglais?

Scene X: To accentuate Henry's loneliness Guy Woolfenden supplied music
at once lonely and sad. Henry remains alone on the stage, staring at Harfleur.
As he turns to go, the wall of the breach begins to lower back into position,
revealing Katherine, daughter of the French King. The effect is to make
her seem like a Venus, rising from the waves.

The presence of both characters on stage at this moment lends weight
to her desire to learn English. And it reminds us of a curiously blank area
in Hal/Henry's life through the three plays: he has never had a wife or
a mistress: he rarely even mentions women. That possibility in his life has
yet to be explored.

The women are a welcome relief. Ludmila Mikaël, who played the role
from the first night to the end of June 1975, is French; Carole Rousseau,
who played subsequently, Belgian; Yvonne Coulette (Alice) is of French
parentage. Between them they modified the text slightly, to incorporate
modern French. The process of bringing two countries together begins here.
Katherine starts to learn the enemy's language. It is a sensual scene, and
her interest is confined to parts of the body. It is funny, if a little coarse.
Katherine misreads 'foot' as 'foutre' or fuck, and gown as 'con' or cunt.
She is shocked. But that doesn't stop her saying it again. And again. Nor
going off to lunch with a good appetite.

ALICE

La main? Elle est appelée de hand.   10

KATHERINE

De hand. Et les doigts?

ALICE

Les doigts? Ma foi, j'oublie les doigts, mais je me souviendrai. Les doigts? Je pense qu'ils sont appelés de fingres; oui, de fingres.

KATHERINE

La main, de hand; les doigts, de fingres. Je pense que je suis le bon écolier; j'ai gagné deux mots d'anglais rapidement. Comment appelez-vous les ongles?

ALICE

Les ongles? Nous les appelons de nailès.

KATHERINE

De nailès. Écoutez: dites-moi si je parle bien – de hand, de fingres, et de nailès.   20

ALICE

C'est bien dit, madame. Il est fort bon anglais.

KATHERINE

Dites-moi l'anglais pour le bras.

ALICE

De arm, madame.

KATHERINE

Et le coude?

ALICE

D'elbow.

KATHERINE

D'elbow. Je m'en fais la repeté de tous les mots que vous m'avez appris jusqu'à présent.

ALICE

Il est trop difficile, madame, comme je pense.

KATHERINE

Excusez-moi, Alice; écoutez – d'hand, de fingre, de nailès, d'arma, de bilbow.   30

ALICE

D'elbow, madame.

KATHERINE

O Seigneur Dieu, j'oublie! D'elbow. Comment appelez-vous le col?

ALICE
De nick, madame.

KATHERINE
De nick. Et le menton?

ALICE
De chin.

KATHERINE
De sin. Le col, de nick; le menton, de sin.

ALICE
Oui. Sauf votre honneur, en vérité, vous prononcez les mots aussi bien que les natifs d'Angleterre.

KATHERINE
Oui, c'est vrai. Je suis sûr de toute apprendre par   40
la grace de Dieu, toute—et en peu de temps.

ALICE
N'avez-vous pas déjà oublié ce que je vous ai enseigné?

KATHERINE
Non, je réciterai à vous promptement: d'hand, de fingre, de mailès—

ALICE
De nailès, madame.

KATHERINE
De nailès, de arm, de ilbow—

ALICE
Sauf votre honneur, d'elbow.

KATHERINE
Ainsi dis-je: d'elbow, de nick, et de sin. Comment appelez-vous le pied et la robe?

ALICE
Le foot, madame, et le count.   50

KATHERINE
Le foot, et le count? O Seigneur Dieu! Ils sont mots de son mauvais, corruptible, gros, et impudique, et non pour les dames d'honneur d'user. Je ne voudrais prononcer ces mots devant les seigneurs de France pour tout le monde. Oh la la! Le foot et le count! Néanmoins, je réciterai une autre fois ma leçon toute entiere: d'hand, de fingre, de nailès, d'arm, d'elbow, de nick, de sin, de foot, le count.

H.V.—L

ALICE
Excellent, madame!

KATHERINE
C'est assez pour une fois. Allons dîner!   60

Scene XI

As Katherine and Alice leave, they pass the
Constable, Montjoy and the Dauphin, who enter

CONSTABLE
'Tis certain he hath passed the river Somme.

MONTJOY
And if he be not fought withal, my lord,
Let us not live in France: let us quit all,
And give our vineyards to a barbarous people.

CONSTABLE
Dieu de batailles! Where have they this mettle?

Scene XI : The text in this scene has been somewhat re-ordered and re-allocated.
The French present a special problem. The cast list names 13 men. Most
have only one scene, sometimes only one line. And their area of the play
is dangerously caricatured. The text they have seems largely disordered. It
has little of the certainty one discovers in the English scenes. Undoubtedly
good professional scenes exist within the welter of this illogicality. But they
need finding. The impression is of several prompt copies lumped into one
final version.

We suspect Shakespeare's own company was about 25 strong. So was
ours. There wasn't room for 13 Frenchmen. So we decided to use the smallest
number possible, and learn more about them.

Obviously the King of France, his son, his herald, his commander-
in-chief—and one other. We chose Orleans.

In this production we gave Montjoy those observations which seemed
suitable to his role as thinker, herald, not warrior.

We gave the more excitable and paranoic Dauphin such inflammatory
statements as existed.

The Constable, a patriot and military man to boot, took the rest. The
Duke of Bretagne, who appears in this scene in the original, was cut. This
together with the real French princesses gave the audience at least the
possibility of evaluating the two sides. The play is not unfair to the French.
The war is perfectly avoidable and perfectly unnecessary. And both sides
know it. It's a study of human error, not human malice.

The line re-organisation was not imposed, but developed in rehearsal.

DAUPHIN

Normans, but bastard Normans, Norman bastards!
O Dieu vivant! Shall a few sprays of us,
The emptying of our father's luxury,
Spirit up so suddenly into the clouds,
And overlook their grafters?   10

CONSTABLE

Mort de ma vie! If they march along
Unfought withal, but I will sell my dukedom
To buy a slobbery and dirty farm,
In that nook-shotten isle of Albion.

DAUPHIN

Our madams mock at us, and plainly say
Our mettle is bred out, and they will give
Their bodies to the lust of English youth,
To new-store France with bastard warriors.

MONTJOY

Is not their climate foggy, raw and dull,
On whom, as in despite, the sun looks pale,   20
Killing their fruit with frowns?

CONSTABLE

Can sodden water
Decoct their cold blood to such valiant heat?
And shall our quick blood, spirited with wine,
Seem frosty?

DAUPHIN

O, for honour of our land,
Let us not hang like roping icicles
Upon our houses' thatch, whiles a more frosty people,
Sweat drops of gallant youth in our rich fields.
        Enter the French King

FRENCH KING

Where is Montjoy the herald? Speed him hence,   30
Let him greet England with our sharp defiance.
Up, princes, and with spirit of honour edged

30–57 The French King is a special case. Traditionally he is played feeble-witted and physically weak. Perhaps because the historical Charles VI was known to have been insane. There is no justification for this in the text. His lines are grave and considered – except here where he represents the aroused warrior-might of France.

Continued on next page.

More sharper than your swords, hie to the field!
Charles Delabreth, high constable of France;
You, Dukes of Orleans, Bourbon, and of Berri,
Alençon, Brabant, Bar, and Burgundy,
Jacques Chatillon, Rambures, Vaudemont,
Beaumont, Grandpré, Roussi, and Faulconbridge,
Foix, Lestrale, Bouciqualt, and Charolais;
High dukes, great princes, barons, lords, and knights,   40
For your great seats now quit you of great shames,
Bar Harry England, that sweeps through our land
With pennons painted in the blood of Harfleur:
Rush on his host, as doth the melted snow
Upon the valleys, whose low vassal seat
The Alps doth spit and void his rheum upon!
Go down upon him, you have power enough,
And in a captive chariot into Rouen
Bring him our prisoner.

DAUPHIN   This becomes the great.   50

FRENCH KING
Therefore, Lord Constable, haste on Montjoy,
And let him say to England that we send
To know what willing ransom he will give.
Prince Dauphin, you shall stay with us in Rouen.

DAUPHIN
Not so, I do beseech your majesty.

FRENCH KING
Now forth, Lord Constable, and Princes all,
And quickly bring us word of England's fall.
Exeunt

Footnote continued from previous page.

His great speech is very strong. An old-style 'tirade'.

In our production he entered in full armour, crowned and helmeted, his voice echoing behind the mask of war. The audience became his war-lords. His appeal is directed at them.

In early club performances we used buskins to increase his symbolic height and power. But since *The Balcony* in 1971 these have become so much an RSC cliché that it was thought best to cut them.

54 Prince Dauphin, you shall stay with us in Rouen. The French King exits to a battle anthem of war horns, trumpets and timpani. His generals exit, in the opposite stage direction, to battle. The Dauphin hesitates between following his father as ordered here, or following the Constable. He follows the Constable. The unity of the French cause is again undermined.

Scene XII

The English camp. Enter English soldiers, Gower and Fluellen

GOWER

Captain Fluellen, Captain Fluellen? Come you from the bridge?

FLUELLEN

I assure you, there is very excellent services committed at the bridge.

GOWER

Is the Duke of Exeter safe?

FLUELLEN

The Duke of Exeter is as magnanimous as Agamemnon, and a man that I love and honour with my soul, and my heart, and my duty, and my live, and my living, and my uttermost power. He is not–God be praised and blessed!–any hurt in the   10 world, but keeps the bridge most valiantly, with

Scene XII: At this point as an extension of the music for the French exit, the canopy emblazoned with the arms of England begins to drop to the floor. It lands reverse-side-up, as a grey puddle of tarpaulin up-stage centre. On to it come Gower and Fluellen. The ideas behind this were complex. We know from the end of Scene IX that the English are sick, tired, and in retreat. Now the full might of France is raised against them. Symbolically their high hope–the heraldic canopy–drops to form a grey and muddy Somme battlefield. The wire hauser supports for the canopy become leafless trees or undergrowth, being cleared by shivering archers, wearing wool ponchoes and 'Stanlingrad' felt boots. The dream has gone, the nightmare reality of war has begun.

Deliberately, however, the scenery is 'on' the stage. It does not cover the whole stage-floor area, and it is far removed from the audience. But finally it contains the whole English army–cold, rebellious, dispirited.

Henry (and the actor playing Henry) has the choice during the scene of joining the army on the canopy, or remaining isolated off it, downstage. For much of the scene he is off the canopy, attempting to reach the men on it with a combination of techniques that have served him in the past–the kingly rhetoric of some of the earlier speeches, and the Boar's Head jokes of the previous plays. The time for such techniques is past: the soldiers realise it; Henry realises it. At the end of the scene he joins them in the mud.

Shakespeare has never left his twin themes of theatre and reality, of real and acted kingship. Neither have we.

excellent discipline. There is an aunchient lieutenant there at the pridge, I think in my very conscience he is as valiant a man as Mark Antony, and he is a man of no estimation in the world, but I did see him do as gallant service.

GOWER
What do you call him?

FLUELLEN
He is called Aunchient Pistol.

GOWER
I know him not.

Enter Pistol

FLUELLEN
Here is the man.   20

PISTOL
Captain, I thee beseech to do me favours.
The Duke of Exeter doth love thee well.

FLUELLEN
Ay, I praise God, and I have merited some love at his hands.

PISTOL
Bardolph, a soldier firm and sound of heart,
And of buxom valour, hath, by cruel fate,
And giddy Fortune's furious fickle wheel,
That goddess blind,
That stands upon the rolling restless stone—

FLUELLEN
By your patience, Aunchient Pistol: Fortune is painted   30
blind, with a muffler afore her eyes, to signify to you
that Fortune is blind, *and she is painted also with a*
wheel, to signify to you, which is the moral of it, that
she is turning, and inconstant, and mutability, and
variation, and her foot, look you, is fixed upon a
spherical stone, which rolls, and rolls, and rolls. In
good truth, the poet makes a most excellent
description of it: Fortune is an excellent moral.

PISTOL
Fortune is Bardolph's foe, and frowns on him;
For he hath stolen a pax, and hangèd must 'a be—
A damnèd death!

ACT I SCENE XII ● 161

Let gallows gape for dog; let man go free,   40
And let not hemp his windpipe suffocate.
But Exeter hath given the doom of death
For pax of little price.
Therefore go speak – the Duke will hear thy voice;
And let not Bardolph's vital thread be cut
With edge of penny cord and vile reproach.
Speak, Captain, for his life, and I will thee requite.

FLUELLEN
Aunchient Pistol, I do partly understand your   50
meaning.

PISTOL
Why, then, rejoice therefor!

FLUELLEN
Certainly, Aunchient, it is not a thing to rejoice at,
for if, look you, he were my brother, I would desire
the Duke to use his good pleasure, and put him to
execution; for discipline ought to be used.

PISTOL
Die and be damned! and 'figo' for thy friendship.

FLUELLEN
It is well.

PISTOL
The fig of Spain!
Exit

FLUELLEN
Very good.

GOWER
Why, this is an arrant counterfeit rascal, I remember
him now. *A bawd, a cutpurse.*   60

FLUELLEN
I'll assure you, 'a uttered as prave words at the pridge
as you shall see in a summer's day. *But it is very
well; what he has spoke to me, that is well, I warrant
you, when time is serve.*

GOWER
Why, 'tis a gull, *a fool*, a rogue, that now and then
goes to the wars, to grace himself at his return into
London under the form of a soldier. *And such fellows
are perfect in the great commanders' names, and they*

*will learn you by rote where services were done: at
such and such a sconce, at such a breach, at such a
convoy; who came off bravely, who was shot, who
disgraced, what terms the enemy stood on; and this they
con perfectly in the phrase of war, which they trick
up with new-tuned oaths*: and what a beard of the
general's cut and a horrid suit of the camp will do
among foaming bottles and ale-washed wits is
wonderful to be thought on. *But you must learn to
know such slanders of the age, or else you may be
marvellously mistook.*

FLUELLEN

I tell you what, Captain Gower; I do perceive he is   70
not the man that he would gladly make show to the
world he is. If I find a hole in his coat, I will tell
him my mind. (*Drum within*) Hark you, the King is
coming, and I must speak with him from the pridge.
      Enter King Henry
God pless your majesty!

KING HENRY

How now, Fluellen, cam'st thou from the bridge?

FLUELLEN

Ay, so please your majesty. The Duke of Exeter has
very gallantly maintained the pridge. The French is
gone off, look you, and there is gallant and most prave
passages. Marry, th'athversary was have possession   80
of the pridge, but he is enforced to retire, and the
Duke of Exeter is master of the pridge. I can tell your
majesty, the Duke is a prave man.

KING HENRY

What men have you lost, Fluellen?

FLUELLEN

The perdition of th'athversary hath been very great,
reasonable great. Marry, for my part, I think the Duke
hath lost never a man, but one that is like to be
executed for robbing a church, one Bardolph, if your
majesty know the man: his face is all bubukles, and
whelks, and knobs, and flames o'fire; and his lips blows   90
at his nose, and it is like a coal of fire, sometimes

blue, and sometimes red; but his nose is executed,
and his fire's out.

KING HENRY

We would have all such offenders so cut off: and we
give express charge, that in our marches through the
country there be nothing compelled from the villages,
nothing taken but paid for, none of the French
upbraided or abused in disdainful language; for when
lenity and cruelty play for a kingdom, the gentler   100
gamester is the soonest winner.

    Enter Montjoy

MONTJOY

You know me by my habit.

KING HENRY

Well then, I know thee: what shall I know of thee?

MONTJOY

My master's mind.

KING HENRY

Unfold it.

MONTJOY

Thus says my King: 'Say thou to Harry of England,
Though we seemed dead, we did but sleep. Advantage

92 His nose is executed, and his fire's out… In our production the responsibility
for Bardolph's death was made firmly Henry's. Fluellen's words were taken as
confident prediction: from his vantage-point upstage of Henry, he could see
that Bardolph was about to die. Exeter entered, and the execution drums
rolled. Exeter looked to Henry for assent, the King gave it, Exeter lowered
his sword, and the execution clearly took place, but off-stage. Thus the final
order for his death was given, unquestionably, by the King who had been
his friend in the Boar's Head days.

    The decision, and the edict that follows it – 'nothing be compelled from
the villages, nothing taken but paid for, none of the French upbraided and
abused in disdainful language…' is clearly unpopular with the soldiers. Henry
is here laying down new rules for his army, which are an extension of the
surprising 'Use mercy to them all' uttered after Harfleur. No longer is pillage
every soldier's right. But this is a radical departure from the accepted code
of war: Henry's army was a volunteer army, and pillage was part of their
pay. Pistol, Nym and Bardolph have already expressed their expectations
of financial gain. Henry is insisting upon a new code, and a new kind of
humanity. We can sympathise with that, and yet we can also, perhaps,
sympathise with Pistol and Bardolph. The world is changing too fast for
them. In the old days Bardolph went raiding on Gadshill with a King's
son. Why should it suddenly change?

is a better soldier than rashness. Tell him we could
have rebuked him at Harfleur, but that we thought
not good to bruise an injury till it were full ripe. Now
we speak upon our cue, and our voice is imperial: 110
England shall repent his folly, see his weakness, and
admire our sufferance. Bid him therefore consider of
his ransom, which must proportion the losses we have
borne, the subjects we have lost, the disgrace we have
digested; which in weight to re-answer, his pettiness
would bow under. For our losses, his exchequer is
too poor; for th'effusion of our blood, the muster of
his kingdom too faint a number; and for our disgrace,
his own person kneeling at our feet but a weak and
worthless satisfaction. To this add defiance: and tell 120
him for conclusion, he hath betrayed his followers,
whose condemnation is pronounced.' So far my King
and master; so much my office.

KING HENRY
What is thy name? I know thy quality.

MONTJOY
Montjoy.

112 following: Montjoy speaks to Henry of his ransom. Until Agincourt
war tended to be an elaborate financial game. The object was not to kill
your opponent, but capture him. He was then released on payment of a
suitable sum, to fight again. The money involved was often enormous. It
was called ransom.

But only aristocrats could afford to pay. So only aristocrats could afford
to play. It was their game. Their rules. The common soldier was their victim.
On the winning side he could expect pillage, booty, and passage to England.
On the losing, his lord would be preserved and ransomed, he would be
killed or left to escape as best he could.

Henry has just executed Bardolph. He has changed the rule concerning
the common soldiers' plunder. He can hardly expect them to be happy. Now
he is faced with another rule, the rule of ransom. He must change that too,
if he is to convince his men that they are one army sharing one destiny.
Harsh to others, he must be harsh to himself. He must prove it is no longer
a game.

Yet the temptation to succumb is there. It takes Henry 15 lines in his
next speech to reach a decision. And nobody believes him. As Bates says
later in the night scene:

"When our throats are cut he may be ransomed, And we ne'er the wiser".

To the disaster of retreat is added the loss of Bardolph, and the cynicism
of his men. Henry is never more alone.

KING HENRY

Thou dost thy office fairly. Turn thee back,
And tell thy King I do not seek him now,
But could be willing to march on to Calais
Without impeachment: for, to say the sooth,
Though 'tis no wisdom to confess so much   130
Unto an enemy of craft and vantage,
My people are with sickness much enfeebled,
My numbers lessened, and those few I have

126–153 Alan Howard (Henry): Montjoy seems to have a knack of entering
and confronting Henry at the woršt possible moment. He does so here just
after the decision to execute Bardolph, and the unpopular edict (it could
not have been otherwise) forbidding plunder. The army is sick, mutinous,
and in retreat. Henry's answers to Montjoy seemed to me from the first
to exhibit very obviously his temporary loss of control, and his uncertainty
about what to do or say next. His first reaction, which is odd, is to ask
Montjoy's name, and to praise his quality, which surely means more than
rank at this point. Montjoy has all the calm that Henry lacks at this moment.
His second is to launch into a speech whose tone throughout is uncertain.
First he says he has no wish to meet the French forces and do battle; then
he attempts what seemed to me feeble jokes, about the comparative merits
of French and English soldiers. Then he says his only ransom is his body,
and reiterates that his army is weak and sick; then he takes a new tack,
and somewhat desperately assures Montjoy that, nonetheless, the English
army 'will come on.' Finally, exacerbated, he repeats all these conflicting–or
anyway tortuous–statements again, as if aware that he has stated them in
a rambling fashion previously. That he exhibits such loss of control, and
loss of skill with words, at such a vital moment, seems to me indicative
of the degree of pain he has suffered at Bardolph's execution, just before.
The moment has come when there is no longer a 'performance' available.

126–159 Alan Howard played the torture of Henry, his indecision and soul
searching. The jokes made no effect upon the tired and sullen soldiery.
Roaming the fore stage almost 'out of frame', caught between the spectators
on the canopy (his army) and the spectators in the audience, he wrestled
with his dual problem of King and actor: whether to continue.
   He decides to step firmly into the scene. He returns to his soldiers. He
commits himself to them. But are they committed to him? I think not.
Otherwise there would be no need for the night scene.
   As Henry orders them on, they shuffle mutinously. Alan Howard splits
the last line in a flash of rage making 'march away' present and imperative.
Angrily he tries to make them sing their battle anthem. They pick it up
reluctantly, raggedly. As they begin to move off, Henry is left to sing alone:
Deo Gracias.
   It is the second use of Guy's army theme tune. The simple patriotism
of Southampton has become bitterly ironic.

Almost no better than so many French;
Who when they were in health, I tell thee, Herald,
I thought upon one pair of English legs
Did march three Frenchmen. Yet forgive me, God,
That I do brag thus! This your air of France
Hath blown that vice in me—I must repent.
Go, therefore, tell thy master here I am;   140
My ransom is this frail and worthless trunk;
My army but a weak and sickly guard:
Yet, God before, tell him we will come on,
Though France himself, and such another neighbour.
Stand in our way. There's for thy labour, Montjoy.
Go bid thy master well advise himself:
If we may pass, we will; if we be hindered,
We shall your tawny ground with your red blood
Discolour: and so, Montjoy, fare you well.
The sum of all our answer is but this: 150
We would not seek a battle as we are,
Nor, as we are, we say we will not shun it.
So tell your master.

MONTJOY

I shall deliver so. Thanks to your highness.
    Exit

GLOUCESTER

I hope they will not come upon us now.

KING HENRY

We are in God's hand, brother, not in theirs.
March to the bridge; it now draws toward night.
Beyond the river we'll encamp ourselves,
And on tomorrow bid them march away.
    Exeunt

ACT II

Enter Chorus

CHORUS

Now entertain conjecture of a time
When creeping murmur and the poring dark
Fills the wide vessel of the universe.
From camp to camp, through the foul womb of night,
The hum of either army stilly sounds,
That the fixed sentinels almost receive
The secret whispers of each other's watch.
Fire answers fire, and through their paly flames
Each battle sees the other's umbered face.
Steed threatens steed, in high and boastful neighs,   10
Piercing the night's dull ear; and from the tents
The armourers, accomplishing the knights,
With busy hammers closing rivets up,
Give dreadful note of preparation.
The country cocks do crow, the clocks do toll,
And the third hour of drowsy morning name.
Proud of their numbers, and secure in soul,
The confident and over-lusty French
Do the low-rated English play at dice,
And chide the cripple tardy-gaited night   20
Who like a foul and ugly witch doth limp
So tediously away.

The opening of the second half: During the interval a second canopy is added
to that used at the end of the first half. The two cover the floor and the
back wall, suggesting the grey mud of this autumn battle-field.

The Chorus speech at the beginning of this act has been divided into
three parts; the first introduces the French; the second, the English; and
the third the battle of Agincourt itself.

167

Scene I

*The night before Agincourt. The lights come up
on the French, centre stage, seated, among the
huddled shapes of the English soldiers, lying at
the sides of the stage.*

CONSTABLE

Tut. I have the best armour of the world. Would it
were day!

ORLEANS

You have an excellent armour; but let my horse have
his due.

CONSTABLE

It is the best horse of Europe.

ORLEANS

Will it never be morning?

DAUPHIN

My Lord of Orleans, and my Lord High Constable,
you talk of horse and armour?

ORLEANS

You are as well provided of both as any prince in
the world.

DAUPHIN

What a long night is this! I will not change my horse   10
with any that treads but on four pasterns. Ça, ha!
He bounds from the earth as if his entrails were
hairs–le cheval volant, le Pegasus, avec les narines
de feu! When I bestride him, I soar, I am a hawk.
He trots the air; the earth sings when he touches it;
the basest horn of his hoof is more musical than the
pipe of Hermes.

ORLEANS

- He's of the colour of the nutmeg.

DAUPHIN

And of the heat of the ginger. It is a beast for Perseus:
he is pure air and fire; and the dull elements of earth   20
and water never appear in him, but only in patient
stillness while his rider mounts him. *He is indeed a
horse, and all other jades you may call beasts.*

CONSTABLE
Indeed, my lord, it is a most absolute and excellent
horse.
DAUPHIN
It is the prince of palfreys; his neigh is like the bidding
of a monarch, and his countenance enforces homage.
ORLEANS
No more, cousin.
DAUPHIN
Nay, the man hath no wit that cannot, from the rising
of the lark to the lodging of the lamb, vary deserved
praise on my palfrey. It is a theme as fluent as the   30
sea: turn the sands into eloquent tongues, and my
horse is argument for them all. 'Tis a subject for a
sovereign to reason on, and for a sovereign's sovereign
to ride on; and for the world, familiar to us and
unknown, to lay apart their particular functions and
wonder at him. I once writ a sonnet in his praise,
and began thus: 'Wonder of nature –'.
ORLEANS
I have heard a sonnet begin so to one's mistress.
DAUPHIN
Then did they imitate that which I composed to my
courser, for my horse is my mistress.   40
ORLEANS
Your mistress bears well.
DAUPHIN
Me well, which is the prescript praise and perfection
of a good and particular mistress.
CONSTABLE
Nay, for methought yesterday your mistress shrewdly
shook your back.
DAUPHIN
So perhaps did yours.
CONSTABLE
Mine was not bridled.
DAUPHIN
O, then belike she was old and gentle, and you rode
like a kern of Ireland, your French hose off, and in
your strait strossers.   50

CONSTABLE
You have good judgement in horsemanship.

DAUPHIN
*Be warned by me, then: they that ride so, and ride not
warily, fall into foul bogs.* I had rather have my horse
to my mistress.

CONSTABLE
I had as lief have my mistress a jade.

DAUPHIN
I tell thee, Constable, my mistress wears his own hair.

CONSTABLE
I could make as true a boast as that, if I had a sow
to my mistress.

DAUPHIN
'Le chien est retourné à son propre vomissement, et la
truie lavée au bourbier': thou mak'st use of anything.

CONSTABLE
Yet do I not use my horse for my mistress, or any   60
such proverb so little kin to the purpose.

MONTJOY
My Lord Constable, the armour that I saw in your
tent tonight–are those stars or suns upon it?

CONSTABLE
Stars, my lord.

DAUPHIN
Some of them will fall tomorrow, I hope.

CONSTABLE
And yet my sky shall not want.

DAUPHIN
*That may be, for you bear a many superfluously, and
'twere more honour some were away.*

CONSTABLE
*E'en as your horse bears your praises, who would trot
as well were some of your brags dismounted.*

62 Here, and throughout the scene, Montjoy is substituted for Rambures.
There is some textual uncertainty in any case about the allocation of the
speeches, and retaining Montjoy rather than introducing a new character
helps to make each individual on the French side identifiable. The lines
flesh out a quality we have already seen in Montjoy–that of a peacemaker,
and point up, in contrast, the arrogance of the professional soldier–the
Constable.

DAUPHIN
*Would I were able to load him with his desert! Will
it never be day?* I will ride tomorrow a mile, and my
way shall be paved with English faces. Will it never
be day!

CONSTABLE
*I will not say so, for fear I should be faced out of my
way; but I would it were morning, for I would fain
be about the ears of the English.*

RAMBURES
Who will go to hazard with me for twenty prisoners?

CONSTABLE
You must first go yourself to hazard ere you have them.

DAUPHIN
'Tis midnight: I'll go arm myself.   70
        Exit

ORLEANS
The Dauphin longs for morning.

MONTJOY
He longs to eat the English.

CONSTABLE
I think he will eat all he kills.

ORLEANS
By the white hand of my lady, he's a gallant prince.

CONSTABLE
Swear by her foot, that she may tread out the oath.

ORLEANS
He is simply the most active gentleman of France.

CONSTABLE
Doing is activity, and he will still be doing.

ORLEANS
He never did harm, that I heard of.

CONSTABLE
Nor will do none tomorrow: he will keep that good
name still.   80

ORLEANS
I know him to be valiant.

72 He longs to eat the English: This can be kindly – the older, more experienced
courtier, comprehending the apprehension/excitement of the fledgling
Dauphin.

CONSTABLE

I was told that, by one that knows him better than you.

ORLEANS

What's he?

CONSTABLE

Marry, he told me so himself, and he said he cared not who knew it.

ORLEANS

He needs not; it is no hidden virtue in him.

CONSTABLE

By my faith, sir, but it is; never anybody saw it but his lackey. 'Tis a hooded valour, and when it appears it will bate.

ORLEANS

Ill will never said well. 90

CONSTABLE

I will cap that proverb with 'There is flattery in friendship'.

ORLEANS

And I will take that up with 'Give the devil his due'.

CONSTABLE

Well placed! There stands your friend for the devil. Have at the very eye of that proverb with 'A pox of the devil'.

ORLEANS

You are the better at proverbs by how much 'A fool's bolt is soon shot'.

86 following: The cuts here are questionable, but we have already seen that the Dauphin and the Constable dislike each other. Enough text remains to show that the Constable has aroused Orlean's disapproval, and Montjoy's apprehension: as a leader the Constable is unable to arouse even simple friendliness. Disunity is bound to follow.

99 My Lord High Constable... The lines of a messenger are here given to the Dauphin. The demolition of the Dauphin is more interesting than the demolition of a new and non-returning character, and the lines fit very aptly the man we have just seen. The interchange that follows emphasises that even after Orleans' mild reproof, the Constable is unrepentant, and unable to accept advice. Everything he does and says maintains his professional and public image, in the traditional mould. The battle to be fought will not be traditional.

CONSTABLE
You have shot over.

ORLEANS
'Tis not the first time you were overshot.
    Enter the Dauphin

DAUPHIN
My Lord High Constable, the English lie within fifteen
hundred paces of your tent.   100

CONSTABLE
Who hath measured the ground?

DAUPHIN
The Lord Grandpré.
    Exit

CONSTABLE
A valiant and most expert gentleman. Would it were
day! Alas, poor Harry of England! He longs not for
the dawning as we do.

ORLEANS
What a wretched and peevish fellow is this King of
England, to mope with his fat-brained followers so
far out of his knowledge.

CONSTABLE
If the English had any apprehension, they would run
away.

ORLEANS
That they lack; for if their heads had any intellectual 110
armour, they could never wear such heavy head-pieces.

MONTJOY
That island of England breeds very valiant creatures:
their mastiffs are of unmatchable courage.

ORLEANS
Foolish curs, that run winking into the mouth of a
Russian bear, and have their heads crushed like rotten
apples! You may as well say that's a valiant flea that
dare eat his breakfast on the lip of a lion.

---

112 Again Montjoy speaks Rambures' lines. The only Frenchman to have
met the English, he is given the chance to ruminate on their more dangerous
qualities. It emphasizes the Constable's refusal to envisage anything but easy
victory.

CONSTABLE
　　Just, just: and the men do sympathize with the mastiffs
　　in robustious and rough coming on, leaving their wits
　　with their wives.

MONTJOY
　　They give them great meals of beef, and iron and　120
　　steel; they eat like wolves, and fight like devils.

ORLEANS
　　Ay, but these English are shrewdly out of beef.

CONSTABLE
　　Then shall we find tomorrow they have only stomachs
　　to eat, and none to fight. Now is it time to arm. Come,
　　shall we about it?

ORLEANS
　　It is now three o'clock: but, let me see–by ten
　　We shall have each a hundred Englishmen.
　　　　Exeunt
　　　　Enter Chorus

CHORUS
　　The poor condemnèd English,
　　Like sacrifices, by their watchful fires
　　Sit patiently, and inly ruminate
　　The morning's danger; and their gesture sad,
　　Investing lank-lean cheeks and war-worn coats,
　　Presenteth them unto the gazing moon
　　So many horrid ghosts. O now, who will behold
　　The royal Captain of this ruined band
　　Walking from watch to watch, from tent to tent,
　　Let him cry, 'Praise and glory on his head!'　　　10
　　For forth he goes and visits all his host,
　　Bids them good morrow with a modest smile,
　　And calls them brothers, friends, and countrymen.
　　Upon his royal face there is no note
　　How dread an army hath enrounded him,
　　Nor doth he dedicate one jot of colour
　　Unto the weary and all-watchèd night,
　　But freshly looks, and overbears attaint
　　With cheerful semblance and sweet majesty;
　　That every wretch, pining and pale before,　　　20
　　Beholding him, plucks comfort from his looks.

A largess universal, like the sun,
His liberal eye doth give to every one,
Thawing cold fear, that mean and gentle all
Behold, as may unworthiness define,
A little touch of Harry in the night.

Scene II

During the Chorus speech (Chorus in follow-spot)
Henry moves slowly downstage among his sleeping
soldiers, a silhouette in the gloom.

KING HENRY

Gloucester, 'tis true that we are in great danger:
The greater therefore should our courage be.
Good morrow, brother Clarence. God Almighty!
There is some soul of goodness in things evil,
Would men observingly distil it out;
For our bad neighbour makes us early stirrers,
Which is both healthful, and good husbandry.
Besides, they are our outward consciences,
And preachers to us all, admonishing
That we should dress us fairly for our end.   10
Thus may we gather honey from the weed,
And make a moral of the devil himself.
          Enter Erpingham
Good morrow, old Sir Thomas Erpingham!
A good soft pillow for that good white head
Were better than a churlish turf of France.

ERPINGHAM

Not so, my liege–this lodging likes me better,
Since I may say, 'Now lie I like a king.'

1–26 Chorus: The second part of the Chorus is used here to introduce and
comment upon Henry. Curiously, everything the Chorus says is belied by
the scene that follows. This was the Folio position for this section of the
speech anyway; and by placing it immediately before the English night scene,
the contrast between the kingly exterior the Chorus describes, and the Henry
we see, is heightened.

Scene II 3 The original line reads, 'Good morrow, brother Bedford'. It was
changed to Clarence, as, in our production, this brother replaced the older
Bedford. For reasons see note, Act 1, Scene II, 116–122.

KING HENRY
'Tis good for men to love their present pains
Upon example: so the spirit is eased;
And when the mind is quickened, out of doubt   20
The organs, though defunct and dead before,
Break up their drowsy grave and newly move
With casted slough and fresh legerity.
Lend me thy cloak, Sir Thomas. Brothers both,
Commend me to the princes in our camp;
Do my good morrow to them, and anon
Desire them all to my pavilion.

GLOUCESTER
We shall, my liege.

ERPINGHAM
Shall I attend your grace?

KING HENRY   No, my good knight.
Go with my brothers to my lords of England.   30
I and my bosom must debate awhile,
And then I would no other company.

ERPINGHAM
The Lord in heaven bless thee, noble Harry!

KING HENRY
God-a-mercy, old heart, thou speak'st cheerfully.
*Henry is left alone on stage, with his sleeping
soldiers. He nudges the recumbent form of Pistol
awake.*

PISTOL
Qui va là?

KING HENRY
A friend.

PISTOL
Discuss unto me, art thou officer,
Or art thou base, common, and popular?

KING HENRY
I am a gentleman of a company.

PISTOL
Trail'st thou the puissant pike?   40

16–17 and 33 It is interesting that for the first time in three plays, an old
man, a man of the previous era, actually approves of Henry. It perhaps
gives him courage in his further actions.

KING HENRY

    Even so. What are you?

PISTOL

    As good a gentleman as the Emperor.

KING HENRY

    Then you are a better than the King.

PISTOL

    The King's a bawcock, and a heart of gold,
    A lad of life, an imp of fame;
    Of parents good, of fist most valiant.
    I kiss his dirty shoe, and from heartstring
    I love the lovely bully. What is thy name?

KING HENRY

    Harry le Roy.

PISTOL

    Le Roy? A Cornish name. Art thou of Cornish crew?   50

KING HENRY

    No, I am a Welshman.

PISTOL

Know'st thou Fluellen?

KING HENRY

    Yes.

PISTOL

    Tell him I'll knock his leek about his pate
    Upon Saint Davy's day.

KING HENRY

    Do not you wear your dagger in your cap that day,
    lest he knock that about yours.

PISTOL

    Art thou his friend?

KING HENRY

    And his kinsman too.

PISTOL

    The 'figo' for thee then!   60

KING HENRY

    I thank you. God be with you!

PISTOL

    My name is Pistol called.

        Exit

KING HENRY

It sorts well with your fierceness.

> *Fluellen and Gower, backstage, begin to argue.*

GOWER

Captain Fluellen!

FLUELLEN

So! In the name of Jesu Christ, speak fewer. It is the greatest admiration in the universal world, when the true and aunchient prerogatifes and laws of the wars is not kept. If you would take the pains but to examine the wars of Pompey the Great, you shall find, I warrant you, that there is no tiddle-taddle nor pibble-pabble 70 in Pompey's camp. I warrant you, you shall find the ceremonies of the wars, and the cares of it, and the forms of it, and the sobriety of it, and the modesty of it, to be otherwise.

GOWER

Why, the enemy is loud, you hear him all night.

FLUELLEN

If the enemy is an ass, and a fool, and a prating coxcomb, is it meet, think you, that we should also, look you, be an ass, and a fool, and a prating coxcomb? In your own conscience now?

GOWER

I will speak lower. 80

FLUELLEN

I pray you and beseech you that you will.

> *They lie down to sleep.*

KING HENRY

Though it appear a little out of fashion,
There is much care and valour in this Welshman.

> *Enter three soldiers, John Bates, Alexander Court,*
> *and Michael Williams*

---

84 The following scene between Henry and his soldiers is traditionally played around a brazier, with attendant props of food, drink, something to sit on etc.

We began spartanly with only a single bale. It got in the way. By the first night it was cut.

The scene is surely about psychological discomfort mirroring physical.

COURT

Brother John Bates, is not that the morning which breaks yonder?

BATES

I think it be; but we have no great cause to desire the approach of day.

WILLIAMS

We see yonder the beginning of the day, but I think we shall never see the end of it. Who goes there?

KING HENRY

A friend.   90

WILLIAMS

Under what captain serve you?

KING HENRY

Under Sir Thomas Erpingham.

WILLIAMS

A good old commander, and a most kind gentleman. I pray you, what thinks he of our estate?

KING HENRY

Even as men wrecked upon a sand, that look to be washed off the next tide.

BATES

He hath not told his thought to the King?

KING HENRY

No, nor it is not meet he should. For though I speak it to you, I think the King is but a man, as I am: the violet smells to him as it doth to me; *the element* 100 *shows to him as it doth to me, all his senses have but human conditions.* His ceremonies laid by, in his nakedness he appears but a man; and though his affections are higher mounted than ours, yet when they stoop, they stoop with the like wing. Therefore, when he sees reason of fears, as we do, his fears, out of doubt, be of the same relish as ours are: yet, in reason, no man should possess him with any appearance of fear, lest he, by showing it, should dishearten his army.

BATES

He may show what outward courage he will, but I 110 believe, as cold a night as 'tis, he could wish himself

in Thames up to the neck; and so I would he were,
and I by him, at all adventures, so we were quit here.

KING HENRY

By my troth, I will speak my conscience of the King:
I think he would not wish himself anywhere but where
he is.

BATES

Then I would he were here alone; so should he be
sure to be ransomed, and a many poor men's lives
saved.

KING HENRY

I dare say you love him not so ill to wish him here   120
alone, howsoever you speak this to feel other men's
minds. Methinks I could not die anywhere so
contented as in the King's company, his cause being
just and his quarrel honourable.

WILLIAMS

That's more than we know.

BATES

Ay, or more than we should seek after; for we know
enough if we know we are the King's subjects. If his
cause be wrong, our obedience to the King wipes the
crime of it out of us.

WILLIAMS

But if the cause be not good, the King himself hath   130
a heavy reckoning to make, when all those legs, and
arms, and heads, chopped off in a battle, shall join
together at the latter day, and cry all, 'We died at
such a place'; some swearing, some crying for a
surgeon, some upon their wives left poor behind them,
some upon the debts they owe, some upon their
children rawly left. I am afeared there are few die
well that die in a battle, for how can they charitably
dispose of anything when blood is their argument?
Now, if these men do not die well, it will be a black   140
matter for the King that led them to it, who to disobey
were against all proportion of subjection.

KING HENRY

So, if a son that is by his father sent about merchandise
do sinfully miscarry upon the sea, the imputation of

his wickedness, by your rule, should be imposed upon his father that sent him; *or if a servant under his master's command, transporting a sum of money, be assailed by robbers, and die in many irreconciled iniquities, you may call the business of the master the author of the servant's damnation.* But this is not so. The King is not bound to answer the particular endings of his soldiers, nor the father of his son, nor the master of his servant; for they purpose not their death when 150 they purpose their services. Besides, there is no king, be his cause never so spotless, if it come to the arbitrement of swords, can try it out with all unspotted soldiers. Some, peradventure, have on them the guilt of premeditated and contrived murder; some, of beguiling virgins with the broken seals of perjury; some, making the wars their bulwark, that have before gored the gentle bosom of peace with pillage and robbery. Now, if these men have defeated the law, and outrun native punishment, though they can 160 outstrip men they have no wings to fly from God. War is His beadle, war is His vengeance. *So that here men are punished for before-breach of the King's laws, in now the King's quarrel. Where they feared the death, they have borne life away; and where they would be safe, they perish.* Then if they die unprovided, no more is the King guilty of their damnation than he was before guilty of those impieties for the which they are now visited. Every subject's duty is the King's,

143 following: This crucial speech of Henry's has been quite heavily cut. Quite simply, the speech is too long and, rhythmically, the evening will not stand endless additional parentheses. But I suspect each decade will cut a different section. For us, with memories of *Henry IV Parts I and II*, the father/son simile was stronger than the master/servant. Hence the first cut.

143–167 Alan Howard (Henry): The realisation that War may be an arena, a man's final testing ground, devised by God, is startling. It is even more startling that Henry should go on to say that 'every subject's soul is his own'–a totally heretical statement. He recognizes the individual's responsibility for his actions, and recognises war as the place where that responsibility is put to the ultimate test.

162 following: The second cut is of a paragraph that is very nearly repetitive, which falls somewhat awkwardly after a natural climax.

but every subject's soul is his own. *Therefore should every soldier in the wars do as every sick man in his bed, wash every mote out of his conscience; and dying so, death is to him advantage; or not dying, the time was blessedly lost wherein such preparation was gained; and in him that escapes, it were not sin to think that, making God so free an offer, He let him outlive that day to see His greatness, and to teach others how they should prepare.*

WILLIAMS

'Tis certain, every man that dies ill, the ill upon his own head–the King is not to answer it.

BATES

I do not desire he should answer for me, and yet   170
I determine to fight lustily for him.

KING HENRY

I myself heard the King say he would not be ransomed.

WILLIAMS

Ay, he said so, to make us fight cheerfully: but when our throats are cut he may be ransomed, and we ne'er the wiser.

KING HENRY

If I live to see it, I will never trust his word after.

WILLIAMS

You pay him then! That's a perilous shot out of an elder-gun, that a poor and a private displeasure can do against a monarch! You may as well go about to turn the sun to ice, with fanning in his face with   180
a peacock's feather. You'll never trust his word after! Come, 'tis a foolish saying.

KING HENRY

Your reproof is something too round. I should be angry with you, if the time were convenient.

---

167 following: The third cut removes an aspect of Elizabethan Christian belief to focus upon a more general concept of "soul". Should Christianity ever regain its ubiquity, some argument might be countenanced for its re-inclusion.

All these cuts were made late in the day, as actors are unsympathetic to cuts.

They are largely unsympathetic to large cuts.

WILLIAMS
    Let it be a quarrel between us, if you live.

KING HENRY
    I embrace it.

WILLIAMS
    How shall I know thee again?

KING HENRY
    Give me any gage of thine, and I will wear it in my
    bonnet: then, if ever thou dar'st acknowledge it, I   190
    will make it my quarrel.

WILLIAMS
    Here's my glove: give me another of thine.

KING HENRY
    There.

WILLIAMS
    This will I also wear in my cap. If ever thou come
    to me and say, after tomorrow, 'This is my glove,'
    by this hand, I will take thee a box on the ear.

KING HENRY
    If ever I live to see it, I will challenge it.

WILLIAMS
    Thou dar'st as well be hanged.

KING HENRY
    Well, I will do it, though I take thee in the King's
    company.   200

BATES
    Be friends, you English fools, be friends! We have
    French quarrels enow, if you could tell how to reckon.

---

183 Your reproof is something too round… Alan Howard (Henry): It seemed
to me possible that Henry was aware of the insufficiency of his own arguments
to Williams, and that this had angered him, as it does people when they
know they have been forced into a defence that they don't totally believe.
Accordingly I broke the line after 'Your reproof is something too round',
then collected myself and continued. The first line retreats into old-fashioned
arrogance as a defence—how dare a common soldier speak like this. The
second is more cautious and considered. Henry checks himself; he cannot
reprove Williams for speaking thus to a King, when he is not a King. Perhaps
he should not reprove him, even if Williams were aware of his identity.
The role-playing of an ordinary man forces him to re-consider his role as
King.

WILLIAMS

Keep they word. Fare thee well.

Exeunt the three soldiers

KING HENRY

*Indeed, the French may lay twenty French crowns to
one they will beat us, for they bear them on their
shoulders; but it is no English treason to cut French
crowns, and tomorrow the King himself will be a clipper.*
Upon the King! Let us our lives, our souls,
Our debts, our careful wives,
Our children, and our sins, lay on the King!
We must bear all. O hard condition,
Twin-born with greatness, subject to the breath
Of every fool, whose sense no more can feel
But his own wringing! What infinite heart's ease   210
Must kings neglect that private men enjoy!
And what have kings that privates have not too,
Save ceremony, save general ceremony?
And what art thou, thou idol ceremony?
What kind of god art thou, that suffer'st more
Of mortal griefs than do thy worshippers?
What are thy rents? What are thy comings-in?
O ceremony, show me but thy worth!
What is thy soul of adoration?
Art thou aught else but place, degree, and form,   220
Creating awe and fear in other men?
Wherein thou art less happy, being feared,
Than they in fearing.
What drink'st thou oft, instead of homage sweet,
But poisoned flattery? O, be sick, great greatness,
And bid thy ceremony give thee cure!
Thinks thou the fiery fever will go out
With titles blown from adulation?
Will it give place to flexure and low bending?
Canst thou, when thou command'st the beggar's knee,   230
Command the health of it? No, thou proud dream,
That play'st so subtly with a king's repose.
I am a king that find thee, and I know
'Tis not the balm, the sceptre, and the ball,
The sword, the mace, the crown imperial,

The intertissued robe of gold and pearl,
The farcèd title running fore the king,
The throne he sits on, nor the tide of pomp
That beats upon the high shore of this world –
No, not all these, thrice-gorgeous ceremony,   240
Not all these, laid in bed majestical,
Can sleep so soundly as the wretched slave,
Who, with a body filled, and vacant mind,
Gets him to rest, crammed with distressful bread;
Never sees horrid night, the child of hell,
But, like a lackey, from the rise to set,
Sweats in the eye of Phoebus, and all night
Sleeps in Elysium; next day after dawn
Doth rise and help Hyperion to his horse
And follows so the ever-running year   250
With profitable labour to his grave:
And but for ceremony, such a wretch,
Winding up days with toil, and nights with sleep,
Had the fore-hand and vantage of a king.
The slave, a member of the country's peace,
Enjoys it, but in gross brain little wots
What watch the king keeps to maintain the peace,
Whose hours the peasant best advantages.

ERPINGHAM
My lord, your nobles, jealous of your absence,
Seek through your camp to find you.
KING HENRY   *Good old knight,*
Collect them all together at my tent.
I'll be before thee.
ERPINGHAM   *I shall do't, my lord.*

---

258 following: The Erpingham sequence, which we cut, seems merely mechanical. At a time when acting was different it may have served as a bridge for the actor between the end of the soliloquy and the beginning of the prayer. Today it is in danger of breaking not just the concentration of the actor, but also that of the audience. Naturalistic bridges are really not necessary to communicate changes of thought, either on stage, or in life. A clanking figure would have been a gross intrusion, and would almost certainly have produced a barrage of released-tension-coughing–timed precisely to drown the vitally important 'O God of battles' that follows immediately after.

KING HENRY

O God of battles, steel my soldiers' hearts;
Possess them not with fear; take from them now   260
The sense of reckoning, lest th'opposèd numbers
Pluck their hearts from them. Not today, O Lord,
O not today, think not upon the fault
My father made in compassing the crown!
I Richard's body have interrèd new,
And on it have bestowed more contrite tears
Than from it issued forcèd drops of blood.
Five hundred poor I have in yearly pay,
Who twice a day their withered hands hold up
Toward heaven, to pardon blood: and I have built 270
Two chantries where the sad and solemn priests
Sing still for Richard's soul. More will I do,
Though all that I can do is nothing worth,
Since that my penitence comes after all,
Imploring pardon.
            Gloucester's voice is heard.

GLOUCESTER

My liege! My liege!

KING HENRY

My brother Gloucester's voice? Ay,
I know thy errand, I will go with thee.
The day, my friends, and all things stay for me.
            He lies down with his soldiers to sleep.

260 Possess them not with fear... Alan Howard (Henry): Interestingly, Henry turns, somewhat superstitiously, to God at this point. I think he is afraid. The enormity of the next day's undertaking has hit him, and so has the realisation of what it could mean to men like Williams and Bates. The realisation makes him first bitter – he refers to their 'gross brains' and lack of comprehension of his own predicament in the ceremony speech – then terror-struck. What will happen the next day? In desperation he appeals to a war-god ('O God of battles') and his first request is that, at least, his men should be spared the sense of reckoning. He does not want *them* to share his awareness of the weakness of their position. The words could be devious – soldiers unaware of the fearful odds may fight more valiantly. But their emotion is very strong; I think they are truly charitable. Henry does not want his men to suffer the fear he feels at this point.

279 The day, my friends, and all things stay for me. Alan Howard (Henry): In the previous scene Henry has been made to realise the full weight of his responsibility as King. The decision he has taken earlier, after asking

Scene III

Enter the Dauphin and Orleans, in golden armour.

ORLEANS

The sun doth gild our armour: up, my lords!

DAUPHIN

Montez à cheval! My horse! Varlet! Lacquais! Ha!

ORLEANS

O brave spirit!

DAUPHIN

Via! Les eaux et la terre!

'May I with right and conscience make this claim?', means life or death to men like Williams, Bates, and Court. A night spent in disguise forces him to re-examine his identity. He must be *himself*, recognising his own responsibilities, and those of others. Only then can his army, following his example, change itself internally. This potential strength could be every body's physical and social salvation: the appeals to God, an exterior force that may bring him victory, are over.

Scene III: The French here are presented in golden armour. (For Arts Council readers, I hasten to add, ordinary armour with gold paper stuck on). Such armour became a theme of all three plays during the course of the season–unusually, an evolved theme, rather than a pre-conception. It grew largely from Alan Howard's awareness of Hal's lines in *Henry IV Part II*–'O majesty/When thou dost pinch thy bearer, thou dost sit/Like a rich armour worn in heat of day/That scald'st with safety' and from Emrys James' almost metaphysical relationship with his own 'death-dealing' crown as Henry IV. So the French knights, le Fer, and Henry V, for his coronation, all wear golden armour. All representative of an outmoded aristocratic ideal and penance. The last flourish of a declining mediaevalism. Henry V is to redefine his kingship not in terms of gold, or armour, but the Renaissance ideals of the complete man: 'the courtier's, soldier's, scholar's, eye, tongue, sword'.

The text of Scene III has been largely re-structured. No lines are added, but they are re-ordered, and re-allocated. Again, I have tried to bring out the humanity, or at least three-dimensional quality of the French by giving the lines of Grandpré to Montjoy. Simply, we follow more logically the career of the men we have already met in the night scene, and the lines are re-arranged to follow the indications of their personalities revealed there. The Constable is still scornful; the Dauphin still over-excited; Montjoy is still the only Frenchman to see the English with clear, not arrogant, eyes. But it is, perhaps, now easier to focus on what the text actually holds: the double view of war as glory and war as carrion. Even the Constable acknowledges (however ironically) the bitterness of empty victory: 'A very little, little let us do/And all is done'.

ORLEANS
    L'air et le feu?

DAUPHIN
    Ciel, cousin Orleans!
      Enter the Constable
    Now, my Lord Constable!

CONSTABLE
    To horse, you gallant Princes, straight to horse!

DAUPHIN
    Mount them and make incision in their hides,
    That their hot blood may spin in English eyes   10
    And dout them with superflous courage, ha!

ORLEANS
    What, will you have them weep our horses' blood?
    How shall we then behold their natural tears?
      Enter Montjoy

MONTJOY
    The English are embattail'd, you French peers.

CONSTABLE
    Yon island carrion desperate of their bones,
    Ill favour'dly become the morning field.
    There is not work enough for all our hands;
    Scarce blood enough in all their sickly veins
    To give each naked curtle-axe a stain.
    Let us but blow on them,   20
    The vapour of our valour will o'erturn them.
    Why our superflous lackeys, and our peasants,
    Who in unnecessary action swarm
    About our squares of battle, were enow
    To purge this field of such a hilding foe.
    Though we upon this mountain's basis by
    Took stand for idle speculation.

DAUPHIN
    But that our honours must not. Come, come away!
    The sun is high, and we outwear the day.

MONTJOY
    Do but behold yon poor and starvèd band.
    Big Mars seems bankrupt in their beggared host,
    And faintly through a rusty beaver peeps.   30
    The horsemen sit like fixèd candlesticks,

With torch-staves in their hands; and their poor jades
Lob down their heads, dropping the hides and hips,
The gum down-roping from their pale-dead eyes,
And in their palèd mouths the gimmaled bit
Lies foul with chawed grass, still and motionless;
And their executors, the knavish crows,
Fly o'er them all, impatient for their hour.
Description cannot suit itself in words
To demonstrate the life of such a battle   40
In life so lifeless as it shows itself.

ORLEANS
They have said their prayers, and they stay for death.

DAUPHIN
Shall we go send them dinners, and fresh suits,
And give their fasting horses provender,
And after fight with them?

CONSTABLE   What's to say?
A very little little let us do,
And all is done. Then let the trumpets sound
The tucket sonance and the note to mount;
For our approach shall so much dare the field
That England shall couch down in fear and yield   50
    Exeunt

Scene IV

*The French exit to an anthem of brass and
kettledrum. The English army wakes unwillingly
to reveille–a ladle banged on a soup-pot. They
begin their day's preparations, rolling blankets,
assembling weapons, etc.*

GLOUCESTER
Where is the King?

CLARENCE
The King himself is rode to view their battle.

WESTMORLAND
Of fighting men they have full three-score thousand.

EXETER
There's five to one: besides, they all are fresh.

CLARENCE (*SALISBURY*)

> God's arm strike with us! 'Tis a fearful odds.
> *God bye you, Princes all: I'll to my charge.*
> *If we no more meet till we meet in heaven,*
> *Then joyfully, my noble Lord of Bedford,*
> *My dear Lord Gloucester, and my good Lord Exeter,*
> *And my kind kinsman, warriors all, adieu!*

BEDFORD

> *Farewell, good Salisbury, and good luck go with thee!*

EXETER

> *Farewell, kind lord: fight valiantly today–*
> *And yet I do thee wrong to mind thee of it,*
> *For thou art framed of the firm truth of valour.*
>
> (*Exit Salisbury*)

BEDFORD

> *He is as full of valour as of kindness,*
> *Princely in both.*

WESTMORELAND

> O that we now had here
> But one ten thousand of those men in England
> That do no work today!

KING HENRY   What's he that wishes so?

> My cousin Westmoreland? No, my fair cousin.
> If we are marked to die, we are enow   10
> To do our country loss: and if to live,
> The fewer men, the greater share of honour.
> God's will! I pray thee wish not one man more.
> By Jove, I am not covetous for gold,
> Nor care I who doth feed upon my cost;
> It yearns me not if men my garments wear;
> Such outward things dwell not in my desires.
> But if it be a sin to covet honour,
> I am the most offending soul alive.
> No, faith, my coz, wish not a man from England: 20
> God's peace! I would not lose so great an honour
> As one man more methinks would share from me

5 following: Again Clarence speaks Bedford's lines, and one of Salisbury's who did not appear in our production.

For the best hope I have. O, do not wish one more!
Rather proclaim it, Westmoreland, through my host,
That he which hath no stomach to this fight,
Let him depart: his passport shall be made,
And crowns for convoy put into his purse.
We would not die in that man's company
That fears his fellowship to die with us.
This day is called the Feast of Crispian: 30
He that outlives this day, and comes safe home,
Will stand a-tiptoe when this day is named,
And rouse him at the name of Crispian.
He that shall see this day, and live old age,
Will yearly on the vigil feast his neighbours,
And say, 'Tomorrow is Saint Crispian.'
Then will he strip his sleeve, and show his scars,
And say, 'These wounds I had on Crispin's day.'
Old men forget; yet all shall be forgot,
But he'll remember, with advantages,   40
What feats he did that day. Then shall our names,
Familiar in his mouth as household words,
Harry the King, Bedford and Exeter,
Warwick and Talbot, Salisbury and Gloucester,
Be in their flowing cups freshly remembered.
This story shall the good man teach his son;
And Crispin Crispian shall ne'er go by,
From this day to the ending of the world,
But we in it shall be rememberèd—
We few, we happy few, we band of brothers: 50
For he today that sheds his blood with me
Shall be my brother; be he ne'er so vile,
This day shall gentle his condition;
And gentlemen in England now abed
Shall think themselves accursed they were not here,
And hold their manhoods cheap, whiles any speaks
That fought with us upon Saint Crispin's day.
        Enter Gloucester
GLOUCESTER
My sovereign lord, bestow yourself with speed.
The French are bravely in their battles set,
And will with all expedience charge on us.   60

KING HENRY
All things are ready, if our minds be so.
WESTMORELAND
Perish the man whose mind is backward now!
KING HENRY
Thou dost not wish more help from England, coz?
WESTMORELAND
God's will, my liege, would you and I alone,
Without more help, could fight this royal battle!
KING HENRY
Why, now thou hast unwished five thousand men,
Which likes me better than to wish us one.
You know your places. God be with you all!
Enter Montjoy
MONTJOY
Once more I come to know of thee, King Harry,
If for thy ransom thou wilt now compound,   70
Before thy most assurèd overthrow:
For certainly thou art so near the gulf
Thou needs must be englutted. Besides, in mercy,
The Constable desires thee thou wilt mind
Thy followers of repentance, that their souls
May make a peaceful and a sweet retire
From off these fields, where, wretches, their poor
    bodies
Must lie and fester.
KING HENRY   Who hath sent thee now?

61 All things are ready, if our minds be so: Alan Howard (Henry): It seemed to me that this line, not the Crispin's day speech that preceeds it, was the one rallying call of the scene. It is like Hamlet's 'The readiness is all' or Edgar's 'Ripeness is all'. Henry passes on to his army the discovery he has made at the end of the night scene. They stand or fall by their own conviction, their own spirit. There is no longer any invocation of God. At the end of the scene he seems simply to challenge God–'And, as thou pleasest, God, dispose the day'. The attempt to win God over to the English side–even superstitiously, is over.
69 Montjoy the herald enters with a green branch as badge of his peaceful office. The idea is ancient–that growth and greenness, representing fecundity, symbolise peace. The English must be made aware of what they are giving up. Fecundity in the midst of the barren mud of battle prefigures the theme of the last scene.

MONTJOY
The Constable of France.

KING HENRY
I pray thee bear my former answer back: 80
Bid them achieve me, and then sell my bones.
Good God, why should they mock poor fellows thus?
The man that once did sell the lion's skin
While the beast lived, was killed with hunting him.
A many of our bodies shall no doubt
Find native graves; upon the which, I trust,
Shall witness live in brass of this day's work.
And those that leave their valiant bones in France,
Dying like men, though buried in your dunghills,
They shall be famed; for there the sun shall greet
them,   90
And draw their honours reeking up to heaven,
Leaving their earthly parts to choke your clime,
The smell whereof shall breed a plague in France.
Mark then abounding valour in our English,
That being dead, like to the bullet's crasing,
Break out into a second course of mischief,
Killing in relapse of mortality.
Let me speak proudly: tell the Constable
We are but warriors for the working-day;
Our gayness and our gilt are all besmirched
With rainy marching in the painful field.
There's not a piece of feather in our host—

83–84 The man that once… The Crispin's day speech finally unites the English.
No longer are they linked merely by such external things as birth, status
or nationality; their unity and determination have become 'interior', a state
of mind, and perhaps heart: 'All things are ready if our minds be so'. In
rehearsal the company looked for ways in which this new confidence and
togetherness might be expressed. It was pointed out that the 'lion's skin'
saying was still proverbial on the continent; that, in Europe, once begun,
the phrase hardly needed finishing. Barrie Rutter (Macmorris), an expert
in such matters, observed its relation to English Music Hall. And so finally
it was used in this way on-stage. The King initiates the phrase; the company
completes it. Henry's speech from there grows into a rousing, blackly funny
parody of confident kingship.
    A music-hall moment shared by all, whatever their rank. A game covering
a real brotherhood felt for the first time.

Good argument, I hope, we will not fly—
And time hath worn us into slovenry.   100
But, by the mass, our hearts are in the trim;
And my poor soldiers tell me, yet ere night
They'll be in fresher robes, or they will pluck
The gay new coats o'er the French soldiers' heads,
And turn them out of service. If they do this—
As, if God please, they shall—my ransom then
Will soon be levied. Herald, save thou thy labour;
Come thou no more for ransom, gentle Herald.
They shall have none, I swear, but these my joints,
Which if they have as I will leave 'em them   110
Shall yield them little, tell the Constable.

MONTJOY

I shall, King Harry. And so fare thee well:
Thou never shalt hear herald any more.
        Exit

KING HENRY

I fear thou wilt once more come again for ransom.

WESTMORELAND

My lord, most humbly on my knee I beg
The leading of the vaward.

KING HENRY

Take it, brave coz. Now, soldiers, march away:
And how Thou pleasest, God, dispose the day!
        Exeunt

115: In Shakespeare's text these lines are York's. He was cut from our production and Henry's answer changed from 'Take it, brave York'.
118 The exit from this scene caused problems. For some time during rehearsals the army formed ranks and just marched away. It wasn't a happy idea, but that seemed to be what armies did, and anyway, it got everybody off the stage. The actors didn't like it.

Farrah, the designer, watching rehearsals one day pointed out that his canopies/tarpaulins weren't going to be marchable over, and that eleven people pretending to be 400 looked silly. He suggested a 'guerrilla' style exit, the army sloping off, indian file, at a run. The actors didn't like it.

The problem remained for some time. The actors succeeded in getting off stage, but little else. Basically, they had to stay spread and mobile to suggest larger numbers, and they had to express an interior discipline without necessarily an exterior form. Somehow it was a new army, a newly united army, and professional. But it could not be regimented and traditional.

Enter Chorus

CHORUS

And so our scene must to the battle fly;
Where–O for pity!–we shall much disgrace,
With four or five most vile and ragged foils,
Right ill-disposed in brawl ridiculous,
The name of Agincourt. Yet sit and see,
Minding true things by what their mockeries be.

*He moves slowly back up stage, and the sounds
of the battle are heard. Le Fer enters, in golden
armour, stage right, back. He staggers downstage,
and collapses. Enter Pistol and the Boy.*

Finally shortly before the first performance a compromise emerged: the 'little touch of Harry in the night' might become the touchstone of Henry during the day. As he had united his band of brothers, so he should give a brotherly farewell. Eleven embraces would take too long, so Henry moved up the stage, each of his soldiers touching him as he passed and slipping away individually into the wings. It gave size and purpose to the exit, kept the 'guerrilla' feeling suggested by Farrah, and in its silence reflected grimness and determination. For the first time, victory was possible.

1–6 Chorus: The final lines of the first Chorus speech of the second half found their way here, inevitably.

Shakespeare does not write a naturalistic battle. The play builds up over sixteen nail-biting scenes to climax in two clowns and a boy. It seemed helpful to remind the audience before it was too late that again it was but a play.

Furthermore although an Elizabethan audience may have been able to hold previous information easily in mind through very intense intervening scenes, and even perhaps been able to 'associate' that information as it was received, our experience at Stratford suggests that that rarely happens now. We tend to think 'linearly', step by step.

And so the next step might need preparation. And so we moved the Chorus.

The Chorus speech was followed by a tape-montage of charging horses, flights of arrows and ensuing carnage. It was prepared by the sound operator Bill Graham under the guidance of Guy Woolfenden. Essentially it followed the form of that used in Peter Hall's 1964 production (also prepared by Guy Woolfenden).

It is splendid and unnecessary.

But this is still a period of naturalism in the theatre, and we weren't courageous enough to move too far away from that naturalism too soon. It allowed the audiences' imagination, focused by Emrys James' haunted face, to recreate for each individual the actual battle of Agincourt, before plunging into Shakespeare's. It lasted forty seconds. In ten years time it will no longer be necessary.

Scene V

Pistol holds Le Fer at sword point.

PISTOL
Yield, Cur!

FRENCH SOLDIER
Je pense que vous êtes le gentilhomme de bonne
qualité.

PISTOL
Calitie! 'Calen o custure me!'
Art thou a gentleman? What is thy name? Discuss.

FRENCH SOLDIER
O Seigneur Dieu!

PISTOL
O Signieur Dew should be a gentleman:
Perpend my words, O Signieur Dew, and mark.
O Signieur Dew, thou diest on point of fox,
Except, O Signieur, thou do give to me   10
Egregious ransom.

FRENCH SOLDIER
O, prenez miséricorde! Ayez pitié de moy!

PISTOL
Moy shall not serve: I will have forty moys,
Or I will fetch thy rim out at thy throat
In drops of crimson blood!

FRENCH SOLDIER
Est-il impossible d'échapper la force de ton bras?

PISTOL
Brass, cur?
Thou damnèd and luxurious mountain goat,
Offer'st me brass?

Scene V: This is an inescapably funny scene. We rehearsed it serious, savage,
slow. It just got funnier.

All the humour is in the lines. The symbolic M. le Fer (Mr. Iron), with
little English, meets the most eccentric speaker in the play, with little French,
and proceeds to converse. The clattering of puns drowns that of his armour.

It is yet another step in the learning of each other's language—a theme
which Shakespeare returns to again and again in these three Henry plays.
It begins with the Glendower scene in *Part I*, continues through the scenes
between Henry IV and Hal, pops up in Mistress Quickly's malapropisms
and the dialects of the four captains in Henry V, and will end in the wooing
of a French princess who does 'not speak your England'.

FRENCH SOLDIER
O, pardonne-moy!   20
PISTOL
Say'st thou me so? Is that a ton of moys?
Come hither, boy: ask me this slave in French
What is his name.
BOY
Écoutez: comment êtes-vous appelé?
FRENCH SOLDIER
Monsieur le Fer.
BOY
He says his name is Master Fer.
PISTOL
Master Fer! I'll fer him, and firk him, and ferret him.
Discuss the same in French unto him.
BOY
I do not know the French for fer, and ferret, and
firk.   30
PISTOL
Bid him prepare, for I will cut his throat.
FRENCH SOLDIER
Que dit-il, monsieur?
BOY
Il me commande à vous dire que vous faites vous
prêt, car ce soldat içi est disposé tout à cette heure
de couper votre gorge.
PISTOL
Owy, cuppele gorge, permafoy,
Peasant, unless thou give me crowns, brave crowns;
Or mangled shalt thou be by this my sword.
FRENCH SOLDIER
O, je vous supplie, pour l'amour de Dieu, me
pardonner! Je suis le gentilhomme de bonne maison.   40
Gardez ma vie, et je vous donnerai deux cents écus.
PISTOL
What are his words?
BOY
He prays you save his life. He is a gentleman of a
good house, and for his ransom he will give you two
hundred crowns.

PISTOL
Tell him my fury shall abate, and I
The crowns will take.

FRENCH SOLDIER
Petit monsieur, que dit-il?

BOY
Pour les écus que vous l'avez promis, il est content
à vous donner la liberté, le franchisement.   50

FRENCH SOLDIER
Sur mes genoux je vous donne mille remercîments;
et je m'estime heureux que je suis tombé entre les
mains d'un chevalier, je pense, le plus brave, vaillant,
et très distingué seigneur d'Angleterre.

PISTOL
Expound unto me, boy.

BOY
He gives you upon his knees a thousand thanks; and
he esteems himself happy that he hath fallen into the
hands of one—as he thinks—the most brave, valorous,
and thrice-worthy signieur of England.

PISTOL
As I suck blood, I will some mercy show.   60
Follow me!
        Exit

BOY
Suivez-vous le grand capitaine.
        (*Exit French Soldier*)
I did never know so full a voice issue from so empty
a heart; but the saying is true, 'The empty vessel makes
the greatest sound.' Bardolph and Nym had ten times
more valour than this roaring devil i'th'old play, *that
everyone may pare his nails with a wooden dagger*;
and they are both hanged—and so would this be, if
he durst steal anything adventurously. I must stay
with the lackeys, with the luggage of our camp. The   70
French might have a good prey of us, if he knew
of it, for there is none to guard it but boys.

Scene VI

Enter three French soldiers, their visors down. They
trap the Boy by the baggage cart, and kill him.
They begin to loot the cart: Enter Constable,
Orleans, Dauphin–their armour disfigured by
battle. Montjoy follows them.

CONSTABLE
O diable!

ORLEANS
O Seigneur! Le jour est perdu, tout est perdu!

DAUPHIN
Mort Dieu! Ma vie! All is confounded, all!
Reproach and everlasting shame
Sits mocking in our plumes. O méchante fortune!
    Exeunt the looters
Do not run away!

CONSTABLE   Why, all our ranks are broke.

ORLEANS
Be these the wretches that we played at dice for?

73 The death of the boy: The killing of the Boy (or boys) is a particular
problem. Should it be shown or not, and if so, when?
    The original text is unclear. There the Boy exits at the end of Act IV
Scene IV. Scene V is the French. At the end of Scene VI Henry orders
the English soldiers to kill their French prisoners, and seems to give the
order because the French are re-grouping–'The French have reinforced their
scattered men/Then every soldier kill his prisoners/Give the word through.'
Yet immediately afterwards, in Scene VII, Fluellen and Gower enter indignant
that French deserters should kill the boys guarding the luggage, and Gower
states that because of this, and the sacking of the King's tent, Henry has
ordered the killing of the prisoners–'Wherefore the king most worthily hath
caused every soldier to cut his prisoner's throat.' So which has come first,
the killing of the boys or the killing of the prisoners? In performance if
we are to show either event, then, in fairness, we must show both. But the
positioning of the events will strongly affect the audience's response.
    If the Boy is killed *before* the order to kill the prisoners is given, then
Henry's action seems less harsh. If the Boy is killed *after* the order to kill
the prisoners, Henry seems ruthless, and the killing of the Boy, and the sacking
of the royal tent could be the French army's last act of revenge. Some
productions in the past have shown the Boy being killed first, but by the
Constable and the Dauphin, as they run from the battle.

Continued on next page.

MONTJOY

Is this the King we sent to for his ransom?

DAUPHIN

O perdurable shame! Let's stab ourselves.   10
Shame, and eternal shame, nothing but shame!

CONSTABLE

Disorder that has spoiled us, friend us now!
Let us on heaps go offer up our lives.

DAUPHIN

Let's die in honour! Once more back again!

ORLEANS

We are enow yet living in the field
To smother up the English in our throngs,
If any order might be thought upon.

Footnote continued from previous page.

In the event we chose, for good or ill, to show the killing of the Boy. He was our Francis in *Henry IV Parts I and II*, and was therefore both strongly established, and a representative of Falstaff's group, and Hal's youth.

It seemed logical that he should be killed at the end of his soliloquy and that, when confronted with his dead body, Henry should recognise him.

But who was to do the killing? Not the Constable, the Dauphin or Orleans, because they are brave men trying to reform their ranks, not cowards. So we invented three faceless deserters, who plundered the cart which the English had pushed around in the war sequences, and who then (in silhouette) slew the Boy. The Constable, Orleans, and the Dauphin just witness the action, which seemed to give added sense to the Dauphin's line 'Do not run away!' To rectify the balance, and to avoid unfairness, we played the French nobles as shocked and shamed by the Boy's death. Perhaps the lesson learned too late by the French is that all war finally descends from imagined honour and glory to the debasement of violation and murder: Henry has said earlier 'What rein can hold licentious wickedness/When down the hill he holds his fierce career?'

Henry's response to the killing–'I was not angry since I came to France'–has been moved forward from its original position after the Fluellen/Gower scene to our Scene VII. It is an emotional response, and a ruthless one. He immediately orders the killing of the prisoners, which we showed at the end of our Scene VII. Only one French prisoner is on stage at that point–Le Fer. As both he and the Boy are popular characters, the impact was equivalent. A certain charm has met a harsh reality.

I think Henry is determined that war shall end. I think it is at that moment–'I was not angry'–that he determines it. War must never again be a game–a game played with prisoners ransomed to fight another game. In the play, and only in the play, war is to end.

DAUPHIN
The devil take order now! I'll to the throng.
Let life be short, else shame will be too long!
Exeunt

Scene VII

Enter the English, including Pistol and his prisoner,
Le Fer.

FLUELLEN
Kill the poys and the luggage? 'Tis expressly against
the law of arms.

GOWER
'Tis certain there's not a boy left alive.

KING HENRY
I was not angry since I came to France
Until this instant. Take a trumpet, Brother;
Ride thou unto the horsemen on yon hill
If they will fight with us, bid them come down,
Or void the field: they do offend our sight.

EXETER
The French have reinforced their scattered men!

KING HENRY
Then every soldier kill his prisoners!   10
Give the word through.
Pistol cuts Le Fer's throat. Exeunt, except Gower
and Fluellen, who remain on stage among the
bodies.

Scene VII: The words of this scene have been transposed and put together
from other scenes on either side of it in the original (for reasons see note
Scene V 72 on the killing of the Boy). The long account from Exeter of
the deaths of Suffolk and York, which occurs at this point in Shakespeare's
text has been cut completely. We have no previous knowledge in the play
of Suffolk and York, and the artificiality of the language suggests to me
that it is a later addition to the play: it doesn't feel integral. I'm sure that
statement will be disproved in some other production, but it hasn't been
yet.

Scene VIII

FLUELLEN

'Tis as arrant a piece of knavery, mark you now, as
can be offert—in your conscience now, is it not?

GOWER

The cowardly rascals that ran from the battle ha' done
this slaughter. Besides, they have burnt and carried
away all that was in the King's tent, wherefore the
King most worthily hath caused every soldier to cut
his prisoner's throat. O, 'tis a gallant King!

FLUELLEN

Ay, he was porn at Monmouth, Captain Gower. What
call you the town's name where Alexander the Pig
was born?   10

GOWER

Alexander the Great.

FLUELLEN

Why, I pray you, is not 'pig' great? The pig, or the
great, or the mighty, or the huge, or the magnanimous,
are all one reckonings, save the phrase is a little
variations.

GOWER

I think Alexander the Great was born in Macedon;
his father was called Philip of Macedon, as I take
it.

FLUELLEN

I think it is in Macedon where Alexander is porn.
I tell you, Captain, if you look in the maps of the   20
'orld, I warrant you sall find, in the comparisons
between Macedon and Monmouth, that the situations,
look you, is both alike. There is a river in Macedon,
and there is also moreover a river at Monmouth—it
is called Wye at Monmouth, but it is out of my prains
what is the name of the other river; but 'tis all one,
'tis alike as my fingers is to my fingers, and there
is salmons in both. If you mark Alexander's life well,
Harry of Monmouth's life is come after it indifferent
well; for there is figures in all things. Alexander, God
knows and you know, *in his rages, and his furies, and
his wraths, and his cholers, and his moods, and his*

displeasures, and his indignations, and also being a little   30
intoxicates in his prains, did in his ales and his angers,
look you, kill his best friend Cleitus.

GOWER

Our King is not like him in that: he never killed any
of his friends.

FLUELLEN

It is not well done, mark you now, to take the tales
out of my mouth, ere it is made and finished. I speak
but in the figures and comparisons of it. As Alexander
killed his friend Cleitus, being in his ales and his cups,
so also Harry Monmouth, being in his right wits and   40
his good judgements, turned away the fat knight with
the great-belly doublet–he was full of jests, and gipes,
and knaveries, and mocks: I have forgot his name
now.

GOWER

Sir John Falstaff.

FLUELLEN

That is he. I'll tell you, there is good men porn at
Monmouth.

GOWER

Here comes his majesty.
        Enter King Henry, and the English forces.

KING HENRY

Well have we done thrice valiant countrymen
But all's not done–yet keep the French the field.
        Enter Montjoy

EXETER

Here comes the Herald of the French, my liege.   50

GLOUCESTER

His eyes are humbler than they used to be.

KING HENRY

How now, what means this, Herald? Know'st thou
not

---

30 following: The furies, wraths and cholers line should not have been
cut. I was less aware of its aptness to Alan Howard's performance during
rehearsals, than during the run. I was less aware of its aptness to Alan
Howard, full stop.

That I have fined these bones of mine for ransom?
Com'st thou again for ransom?
MONTJOY   No, great King;
I come to thee for charitable licence,
That we may wander o'er this bloody field
To book our dead, and then to bury them,
To sort our nobles from our common men.   60
For many of our princes–woe the while!–
Lie drowned and soaked in mercenary blood;
So do our vulgar drench their peasant limbs
In blood of princes, and their wounded steeds
Fret fetlock-deep in gore, and with wild rage
Yerk out their armèd heels at their dead masters,
Killing them twice. O, give us leave, great King,
To view the field in safety, and dispose
Of their dead bodies!
KING HENRY   I tell thee truly, Herald,   70
I know not if the day be ours or no;
For yet a many of your horsemen peer
And gallop o'er the field.
MONTJOY   The day is yours.
KING HENRY
Praisèd be God, and not our strength, for it!
What is this castle called that stands hard by?
MONTJOY
They call it Agincourt.
KING HENRY
Then call we this the field of Agincourt,
Fought on the day of Crispin Crispianus.
FLUELLEN
Your grandfather of famous memory, an't please your   80
majesty, and your great-uncle Edward the Plack
Prince of Wales, as I have read in the chronicles, fought
a most prave pattle here in France.

70–74 A battle begun by 3 clowns, fought over boys, luggage and prisoners,
and ended in confusion.
     Where, other then the minds of journalists and academics, is the famed
tub-thumping, war-mongering patriotism?
80–102 It is delightful that a great 'English' victory is celebrated by a Welsh
captain, and, we are informed at once–a Welsh king.

KING HENRY
They did, Fluellen.

FLUELLEN
Your majesty says very true. If your majesties is
remembered of it, the Welshmen did good service in
a garden where leeks did grow, wearing leeks in their
Monmouth caps, which your majesty know to this
hour is an honourable badge of the service; and I
do believe your majesty takes no scorn to wear the   90
leek upon Saint Tavy's day.

KING HENRY
I wear it as a memorable honour;
For I am Welsh, you know, good countryman.

FLUELLEN
All the water in Wye cannot wash your majesty's
Welsh plood out of your pody, I can tell you that.
God pless it and preserve it, as long as it pleases His
grace, and His majesty too!

KING HENRY
Thanks, good my countryman.

FLUELLEN
By Jeshu, I am your majesty's countryman, I care
not who know it; I will confess it to all the 'orld.   100
I need not to be ashamed of your majesty, praised
be God, so long as your majesty is an honest man.

KING HENRY
God keep me so! Cousin of Westmoreland,
Bring me just notice of the numbers dead
On both our parts.
         Exit Westmoreland.
Call yonder fellow hither.

EXETER
Soldier, you must come to the King.

KING HENRY
Soldier, why wear'st thou that glove in thy cap?

WILLIAMS
An't please your majesty, 'tis the gage of one that
I should fight withal, if he be alive.   110

KING HENRY
An Englishman?

WILLIAMS

An't please your majesty, a rascal that swaggered with me last night: who, if 'a live and ever dare to challenge this glove, I have sworn to take him a box o'th'ear. *Or if I can see my glove.in his cap, which he swore as he was a soldier he would wear if alive, I will strike it out soundly.*

KING HENRY

What think you, Captain Fluellen, is it fit this soldier keep his oath?

FLUELLEN

He is a craven and a villain else, an't please your majesty, in my conscience.

KING HENRY

It may be his enemy is a gentleman of great sort, quite from the answer of his degree.

FLUELLEN

Though he be as good a gentleman as the devil is, as Lucifer and Belzebub himself, it is necessary, look your grace, that he keep his vow and his oath. If he be perjured, see you now, his reputation is as arrant a villain and a Jack-sauce as ever his black shoe trod upon God's ground and His earth, in my conscience, la!

KING HENRY

Then keep thy vow, sirrah, when thou meet'st the fellow. 120

WILLIAMS

So I will, my liege, as I live.

KING HENRY

Who serv'st thou under?

WILLIAMS

Under Captain Gower, my liege.

FLUELLEN

Gower is a good captain, and is good knowledge and literatured in the wars.

KING HENRY

Call him hither to me, soldier.

WILLIAMS

I will, my liege.

　　　　Exit

KING HENRY
Here, Fluellen, wear thou this favour for me, and stick
it in thy cap. When Alençon and myself were down
together, I plucked this glove from his helm. If any
man challenge this, he is a friend to Alençon, and
an enemy to our person: if thou encounter any such,   130
apprehend him, an thou dost me love.

FLUELLEN
Your grace doo's me as great honours as can be desired
in the hearts of his subjects. I would fain see the man
that has but two legs that shall find himself aggriefed
at this glove, that is all. *But I would fain see it once,*
and please God of His grace that I might see.

KING HENRY
Know'st thou Gower?

FLUELLEN
He is my dear friend, an please you.

KING HENRY
Pray thee go seek him, and bring him to my tent.

FLUELLEN
I will fetch him.

KING HENRY
My lord of Warwick and my brother Gloucester,
Follow Fluellen closely at the heels.
The glove which I have given him for a favour
May haply purchase him a box o'th'ear.
It is the soldier's: I by bargain should
Wear it myself. Follow, good cousin Warwick.
If that the soldier strike him, as I judge
By his blunt bearing he will keep his word,
Some sudden mischief may arise of it;
For I do know Fluellen valiant,
And, touched with choler, hot as gunpowder,
And quickly will return an injury.
Follow, and see there be no harm between them.
    Exit King Henry

139 following: The King's speech is cut to save time, and because the audience
know what is going to happen without his saying so. These speeches often
turn up in Shakespeare texts: they are really stage directions, and aids to
performance which have crept into the play. If the advice is taken and
incorporated, the lines themselves become unnecessary.

Scene IX

The English army begin to clear the field of battle.
Enter Gower and Williams, who encounter
Fluellen.

WILLIAMS
I warrant it is to knight you, Captain.

FLUELLEN
God's will and His pleasure, Captain, I beseech you
now, come apace to the King. There is more good
toward you, peradventure, than is in your knowledge
to dream of.

WILLIAMS
Sir, know you this glove?

FLUELLEN
Know the glove? I know the glove is a glove.

WILLIAMS
I know this; and thus I challenge it.
  He strikes him

FLUELLEN
'Sblood! an arrant traitor as any's in the universal
world, or in France, or in England!   10

GOWER
How now, sir? You villain!

WILLIAMS
Do you think I'll be forsworn?

FLUELLEN
Stand away, Captain Gower: I will give treason his
payment into plows, I warrant you.

WILLIAMS
I am no traitor.

FLUELLEN
That's a lie! *I charge you in his majesty's name,*
apprehend him: *he's a friend of the Duke Alençon's.*

16 The fight that begins at this point between Fluellen and Williams,
developed, in our production, into a general much-enjoyed brawl, with all
the other soldiers, and with the King's brothers–Gloucester and
Clarence–joining in, and being turfed aside with notable lack of ceremony.
In this post-Agincourt world the barriers which existed at the beginning
of the play, and throughout *Henry IV Parts I and II*, are demolished. 'Bands

WARWICK
> *How now, how now, what's the matter?*

FLUELLEN
> *My Lord of Warwick, here is–praised be God for it!–a*
> *most contagious treason come to light, look you, as you*
> *shall desire in a summer's day. Here is his majesty.*
>> *Enter King Henry*

KING HENRY
> How now, what's the matter?

FLUELLEN
> My liege, here is a villain and a traitor, that, look
> your grace, has struck the glove which your majesty
> is take out of the helmet of Alençon.   20

WILLIAMS
> My liege, this was my glove, here is the fellow of it;
> and he that I gave it to in change promised to wear
> it in his cap. I promised to strike him if he did. I
> met this man with my glove in his cap, and I have
> been as good as my word.

FLUELLEN
> Your majesty hear now, saving your majesty's
> manhood, what an arrant, rascally, beggarly, lousy
> knave it is. I hope your majesty is pear me testimony
> and witness, and will avouchment, that this is the glove
> of Alençon that your majesty is give me, in your   30
> conscience, now.

KING HENRY
> Give me thy glove, soldier. Look, here is the fellow
> of it.
> 'Twas I indeed thou promisèd'st to strike,
> And thou hast given me most bitter terms.

FLUELLEN
> An please your majesty, let his neck answer for it,
> if there is any martial law in the world.

KING HENRY
> What satisfaction canst thou offer me?

---

of brothers' don't often bow to each other. Here, and in the following scenes,
we tried to show how comradeship had brought with it a new understanding
of equality.

WILLIAMS

All offences, my lord, come from the heart: never came
any from mine that might offend your majesty.   40

KING HENRY

It was ourself thou didst abuse.

WILLIAMS

Your majesty came not like yourself: you appeared
to me but as a common man—witness the night, your
garments, your lowliness, and what your highness
suffered under that shape, I beseech you take it for
your own fault, and not mine; for had you been as
I took you for, I made no offence; therefore, I beseech
your highness, pardon me.

KING HENRY

Here, uncle Exeter, fill this glove with crowns,
And give it to this fellow. Keep it, fellow,   50
And wear it for an honour in thy cap
Till I do challenge it. Give him the crowns;
Captain, you must needs be friends with him.

49–53 There are two schools of thought (at least) on Williams and the money.
Some believe that he accepts glove and money without hesitation. Others,
harking back to the night scene, insist that the money is not taken. Fluellen's
line, 'The fellow has mettle enough in his belly', I think proves that he does
take the money eventually. But why he takes it, and at which point in the
speech is another matter. Whether he takes it or refuses it, his action, and
the way in which Henry speaks to him, have strong reverberations throughout
the entire play. If Henry truly expects him to take it, he is being unpardonably
patronising to one of the men who has just laid his life on the line for
him. If Williams accepts it willingly, he accepts the old, hierarchic, obsequious
system that makes such actions possible, at the same time. Neither Alan
Howard nor Dan Meaden (Williams) believed the scene should be played
in that way. An elaborate ceremony was devised between them.

On 'Keep it, fellow', Williams refuses the money. Henry then tips the money
(in a pouch) out of the glove, and on 'And wear it for an honour in thy
cap', taps Williams with the glove on both shoulders, as if to knight him.
'Give him the crowns' became almost humourous. Having established his
integrity, the money could be accepted by Williams, and was. I think the
semi-knighting is over-elaborate. Alan Howard and Dan Meaden will argue
otherwise. I don't agree with them.

49–53 Alan Howard (Henry): What Terry Hands describes as 'over-elaborate'
seems to me to evolve directly from the text of this speech, which makes
little sense if Williams immediately accepts the money. Earlier Henry has
hinted that he will explore the full implications of Williams' challenge, with

FLUELLEN

By this day and this light, the fellow has mettle enough
in his belly. Hold, there is twelve pence for you, and
I pray you to serve God, and keep you out of prawls,
and prabbles, and quarrels, and dissensions, and I
warrant you it is the better for you.

WILLIAMS

I will none of your money.

FLUELLEN

It is with a good will: I can tell you it will serve   60
you to mend your shoes. *Come, wherefore should you
be so pashful?* Your shoes is not so good; 'tis a good
silling, I warrant you, or I will change it.

   Enter Westmoreland

KING HENRY

Now, cousin, are the dead numbered?

WESTMORELAND

Here is the number of the slaughtered French.

   He gives him a paper

KING HENRY

What prisoners of good sort are taken, uncle?

EXETER

Charles Duke of Orleans, nephew to the King;
John Duke of Bourbon, and Lord Bouciqualt;

---

the words 'I embrace it'. In the night he has met a man of what seems
to be–must be–integrity. What follows here is a final testing of that integrity.
Henry for a start uses selfconsciously insulting terms–'fellow', he says to
Williams, twice. Exeter fills the glove with crowns; Henry urges Williams
to accept it. But what exactly happens between this line and the next–'And
wear it for an honour in thy cap...' Is Williams supposed to put the glove,
plus crowns, into his cap? Clearly not. Something else is suggested. Particularly
since Henry then repeats the 'Give him the crowns'. Why would he need
to repeat this if Williams had accepted the money? These textual ambiguities,
together with the fact that Shakespeare has already deliberately introduced
the subject of knighting with Williams 'I warrant it is to knight you, Captain'
seem to me clear evidence that Henry (who likes testing people) is testing
Williams at this point. Williams refuses the money and earns Henry's respect.
He knights him, or prefers him, for this reason. The accepting of the money
then carries no moral implications. It can be a joke.

64 following: These speeches are cut to increase the impact of the reading
of the list of the dead by Henry, which follows.

Of other lords and barons, knights and squires,
Full fifteen hundred, besides common men.

KING HENRY
This note doth tell me of ten thousand French
That in the field lie slain. Of princes, in this number,
And nobles bearing banners, there lie dead
One hundred twenty-six: added to these,   70
Of knights, esquires, and gallant gentlemen,
Eight thousand and four hundred; of the which,
Five hundred were but yesterday dubbed knights.
So that, in these ten thousand they have lost,
There are but sixteen hundred mercenaries;
The rest are princes, barons, lords, knights, squires,
And gentlemen of blood and quality.
The names of those their nobles that lie dead:
Charles Delabreth, High Constable of France,
Jaques of Chatillon, Admiral of France,
The Master of the Cross-bows, Lord Rambures,
Great Master of France, the brave Sir Guichard
Dauphin,
John Duke of Alençon, Antony Duke of Brabant,
The brother to the Duke of Burgundy,
And Edward Duke of Bar: of lusty earls,
Grandpré and Roussi, Faulconbridge and Foix,   80
Beaumont and Marle, Vaudemont and Lestrale.
Here was a royal fellowship of death!
Where is the number of our English dead?
Westmoreland gives him another paper
Edward the Duke of York, the Earl of Suffolk,
Sir Richard Kikely, Davy Gam, esquire;
None else of name; and of all other men
But five-and-twenty. O God, Thy arm was here!

84–107 For the reading of the English dead, the army clustered together for
the first time.
    For the first time the audience realised just how small the cast was.
87 O God, thy arm was here: Alan Howard (Henry): The odds of the battle,
and the fact that the English have won against them, alter Henry's view
of what has happened. The determination he had and his army had,
before the battle, is not enough to explain what has happened. It is a mystery,
or a miracle. He accepts it as such.

And not to us, but to Thy arm alone,
Ascribe we all! When, without stratagem,
But in plain shock and even play of battle,   90
Was ever known so great and little loss
On one part and on th'other? Take it, God,
For it is none but Thine!
EXETER   'Tis wonderful!
KING HENRY
Come, go we in procession to the village:
And be it death proclaimèd through our host
To boast of this, or take that praise from God
Which is His only.
FLUELLEN
Is it not lawful, an please your majesty, to tell how
many is killed?
KING HENRY
Yes, Captain, but with this acknowledgement,   100
That God fought for us.
FLUELLEN
Yes, my conscience, He did us great good.
KING HENRY
Do we all holy rites:
Let there be sung 'Non Nobis' and 'Te Deum',
The dead with charity enclosed in clay;
And then to Calais, and to England then,
Where ne'er from France arrived more happy men.
        Exeunt. King Henry and Montjoy leave together.
        They pause, and look downstage, back across the
        field of Agincourt.
        (*Enter Chorus*)

107 For the exit from Scene IX Guy Woolfenden was asked for a 'Te Deum'.
Having written a highly successful 'Non nobis' for the '64 production, he
found it difficult. He asked for some words to which he could write his
music. Nobody provided them. He found some for himself. Nobody liked
them.
    He wrote a kind of carol.
    It was kind of rehearsed.
    But it wasn't religious enough nor jubilant enough. In rehearsals the cast
felt that the soldiers would choose a joyful song, the director insisted it
should be humble. Alan Howard wanted something ambiguous.

Continued on next page.

CHORUS

Vouchsafe to those that have not read the story
That I may prompt them; and of such as have,
I humbly pray them to admit th'excuse
Of time, of numbers, and due course of things,
Which cannot in their huge and proper life
Be here presented. Now we bear the King
Toward Calais. Grant him there: there seen,
Heave him away upon your wingèd thoughts
Athwart the sea. Behold, the English beach
Pales in the flood with men, with wives, and boys,   10
Whose shouts and claps outvoice the deep-mouthed
    sea,
Which like a mighty whiffler fore the King
Seems to prepare his way. So let him land,
And solemnly see him set on to London.
So swift a pace hath thought that even now
You may imagine him upon Blackheath,
Where that his lords desire him to have borne
His bruisèd helmet and his bended sword
Before him through the city. He forbids it,
Being free from vainness and self-glorious pride,   20
Giving all trophy, signal, and ostent
Quite from himself to God. But now behold,
In the quick forge and working-house of thought,
How London doth pour out her citizens:
The Mayor and all his brethren in best sort,
Like to the senators of th'antique Rome,
With the plebeians swarming at their heels,

Footnote continued from previous page.

The soldiers then asked to sing their Southampton tune, which they liked
and had learnt. (Or liked because they had learnt.)

But they didn't want to sing the words.

Finally Guy suggested a double song. A traditional 'Te Deum' sung by
Fluellen–a solo voice from the land of Welsh preachers, whyll, and rules
of war, and that below and through it should grow the army's version of
their normal marching song.

Alan Howard found it ambiguous.

As the army curved out and away Henry and Montjoy were left looking
back on the desolation of the battle field. As they left the Chorus came
on and, listening to the end of the song–off stage–began his next chorus.

Go forth and fetch their conquering Caesar in:
As, by a lower but loving likelihood,
Were now the General of our gracious Empress—
As in good time he may—from Ireland coming,
Bringing rebellion broachèd on his sword,
How many would the peaceful city quit
To welcome him! *Much more, and much more cause,*
Did they this Harry. Now in London place him—
As yet the lamentation of the French
Invites the King of England's stay at home.
The Emperor's coming in behalf of France
To order peace between them; and omit
All the occurrences, whatever chanced,
Till Harry's back-return again to France.   30
There must we bring him; and myself have played
The interim, by remembering you 'tis past.
Then brook abridgement, and your eyes advance,
After your thoughts, straight back again to France.

Scene X

The Chorus remains onstage. Enter the English
soldiers, including Fluellen and Gower.

GOWER
Nay, that's right. But why wear you your leek today?
Saint Davy's day is past.

FLUELLEN
There is occasions and causes why and wherefore in
all things. I will tell you ass my friend, Captain Gower:
the rascally, scauld, beggarly, lousy, pragging knave
Pistol—which you and yourself and all the world know
to be no petter than a fellow, look you now, of no

---

28 following. Chorus: These lines were cut because their contemporary
Elizabethan allusions are less relevant today.
Scene X: The beginning of this scene was staged like the striking of a circus
tent. The soldiers came on whistling, attached the wires to the canopy so
that it could be flown for the following scene. There was music, relief and
relaxation. Pistol's and Fluellen's confrontation took place among all the
other English soldiers.

merits–he is come to me and prings me pread and
salt yesterday, look you, and bid me eat my leek. It
was in a place where I could not breed no contention 10
with him; but I will be so bold as to wear it in my
cap till I see him once again, and then I will tell him
a little piece of my desires.

Enter Pistol

GOWER
Why, here he comes, swelling like a turkey-cock.

FLUELLEN
'Tis no matter for his swellings nor his turkey-cocks.
God pless you, Aunchient Pistol! you scurvy, lousy
knave, God pless you!

PISTOL
Ha, art thou bedlam? Dost thou thirst, base Trojan,
To have me fold up Parca's fatal web?
Hence! I am qualmish at the smell of leek. 20

FLUELLEN
I peseech you heartily, scurvy, lousy knave, at my
desires, and my requests, and my petitions, to eat,
look you, this leek. Because, look you, you do not
love it, nor your affections, and your appetites, and
your digestions, doo's not agree with it, I would desire
you to eat it.

PISTOL
Not for Cadwallader and all his goats!

21 **following:** However variable in performance, all productions of *Henry
V* share certain constants–mainly problems–among which is that of the
leek. In the first place, it is not a very appetising vegetable in its raw state,
except, perhaps, to a Welshman. And English actors do tend to play Pistol.
Secondly, it is a seasonable vegetable, that defies deep freezing. Indefatigable
stage management efforts contrived to prolong Pistol's misery into late
summer, but finally even the Vale of Evesham ran out. It then became the
province of the equally indefatigable props department, who began by
providing a lasting substitute of solid steel (without warning), and ended
by creating an impressively leek-like leek of cucumber and plastic.

As the season progressed Ricard Moore's leek got smaller and smaller
(and he spat more of it away), and Trevor (I've got another leek in my
pocket) Peacock's got larger and larger.

The majority of both remained on stage after the scene. Which is the
second constant problem of productions of *Henry V.*

FLUELLEN

There is one goat for you.

(*He strikes him*)

Will you be so good, scauld knave, as eat it?

PISTOL

Base Trojan, thou shalt die!   30

FLUELLEN

You say very true, scauld knave, when God's will is.
I will desire you to live in the meantime, and eat
your victuals–come, there is sauce for it.

(*He strikes him again*)

You called me yesterday mountain-squire, but I will
make you today a squire of low degree. I pray you
fall to–if you can mock a leek, you can eat a leek.

GOWER

Enough, Captain, you have astonished him.

FLUELLEN

I say, I will make him eat some part of my leek, or
I will peat his pate four days. Bite, I pray you, it
is good for your green wound and your ploody
coxcomb.   40

PISTOL

Must I bite?

FLUELLEN

Yes, certainly, and out of doubt, and out of question
too and ambiquities.

CHORUS

Ambiquities.

FLUELLEN

Yes, ambiquities, yes.

PISTOL

By this leek, I will most horribly revenge–I eat and
eat, I swear–

FLUELLEN

Eat, I pray you; will you have some more sauce to
your leek? There is not enough leek to swear by.

PISTOL

Quiet thy cudgel, thou dost see I eat.   50

FLUELLEN

Much good do you, scauld knave, heartily. Nay, pray

you throw none away, the skin is good for your broken
coxcomb. When you take occasions to see leeks
hereafter, I pray you mock at 'em, that is all.

PISTOL
Good!

FLUELLEN
Ay, leeks is good. Hold you, there is a groat to heal
your pate.

PISTOL
Me a groat?

FLUELLEN
Yes, verily and in truth you shall take it, or I have
another leek in my pocket which you shall eat.   60

PISTOL
I take thy groat in earnest of revenge.

FLUELLEN
If I owe you anything, I will pay you in cudgels—you
shall be a woodmonger, and buy nothing of me but
cudgels! God bye you, and keep you, and heal your
pate.

> *Exit all except Gower and Pistol. Gower begins
> to bind Pistol's wounds with an unsavoury poultice
> of leek and bandages.*

PISTOL
All hell shall stir for this!

GOWER
Go, go, you are a counterfeit cowardly knave. Will
you mock at an ancient tradition, begun upon an
honourable respect, and worn as a memorable trophy
of predeceased valour, and dare not avouch in your   70
deeds any of your words? I have seen you gleeking
and galling at this gentleman twice or thrice. You
thought, because he could not speak English in the
native garb, he could not therefore handle an English
cudgel. You find it otherwise, and henceforth let a
Welsh correction teach you a good English condition.
Fare ye well.

> *Exit*

PISTOL
Doth Fortune play the housewife with me now?

News have I that my Nell is dead i'th'spital
Of malady of France,   80
And there my rendezvous is quite cut off.
Old I do wax, and from my weary limbs
Honour is cudgelled. Well, bawd I'll turn,
And something lean to cutpurse of quick hand.
To England will I steal, and there I'll–steal;
And patches will I get unto these cudgelled scars,
And swear I got them in the Gallia wars.
Exit

Scene XI

*Enter, stage right, King Henry, Exeter, Gloucester,
Clarence, and Westmoreland, Enter, stage left, the
French King, the Princess Katherine, Alice, other
French and the Duke of Burgundy.*

KING HENRY
Peace to this meeting, *wherefor we are met!*
Unto our brother France, *and to our sister,*
Health and fair time of day. Joy and good wishes
To our most fair and princely cousin Katherine;

79 In Shakespeare's text as we have it, Pistol says 'News have I that my
Doll is dead i'th'spital'. Most scholars agree that this is a mistake, or, very
possibly, a left-over from a previous version of the play in which Falstaff
may have accompanied Henry to France. Certainly, as Pistol has married
Nell Quickly, he should more logically seek refuge with her. And the news
of her death completes the purge of Falstaff and the other companions of
Hal's youth. Only Pistol survives.

Scene XI: In our production Queen Isabel was cut. Again she is a character
who suddenly appears in a scene, without any previous mention or establishing
of her. It could be argued that she brings additional femininity to what
has been a male-oriented play, thus confronting Henry more forcefully with
peace and with fecundity. On the other hand, she speaks either repetitively,
and should be cut, or heraldically, when her lines can be transferred. We
decided to lose her. Dramatically it makes sense for Henry to end the play
(see note line 253); pedantically, we have perhaps erred.

Burgundy, in our production, was played by the Chorus. I doubt if there
is a Henry alive who has not regretted the deus ex machina, Burgundy,
who arrives with one of the longest speeches in the play, just as the audience
is deciding whether to walk to the last bus, or stay, and run for it. It seemed

Continued on next page.

And, as a branch and member of this royalty,
By whom this great assembly is contrived,
We do salute you, Duke of Burgundy;
And, Princes French, and peers, health to you all!

FRENCH KING
Right joyous are we to behold your face,
Most worthy brother England: fairly met!
So are you, Princes English, every one.

QUEEN ISABEL
So happy be the issue, brother England,
Of this good day, and of this gracious meeting,
As we are now glad to behold your eyes—
Your eyes which hitherto have borne in them,
Against the French that met them in their bent,
The fatal balls of murdering basilisks.
The venom of such looks, we fairly hope,
Have lost their quality, and that this day
Shall change all griefs and quarrels into love.

KING HENRY
To cry 'Amen' to that, thus we appear.

QUEEN ISABEL
You English Princes all, I do salute you.

BURGUNDY
My duty to you both, on equal love,
Great Kings of France and England! *That I have*
        laboured
With all my wits, my pains, and strong endeavours,
To bring your most imperial majesties
Unto this bar and royal interview,
Your mightiness on both parts best can witness.
Since that my labours have so far prevailed   10

Footnote continued from previous page.

to us that Burgundy's language was similar to that of the Chorus; and that Shakespeare, leading us into the last and most important battle of all—that of peace, might reasonably guide us in the same way. Perhaps even with the same person. So Emrys James came forward, still dressed as Chorus, and took Burgundy's lines.

It does not work less well than a separately identifiable Burgundy. The lines are the same. The message is the same. Does it really matter *who* guides Henry, provided he (and we, the audience) is guided? Particularly when it is in a direction in which, clearly, Henry is already going.

That face to face, and royal eye to eye,
You have congreeted, let it not disgrace me
If I demand, before this royal view,
What rub or what impediment there is
Why that the naked, poor, and mangled peace,
Dear nurse of arts, plenties, and joyful births,
Should not in this best garden of the world,
Our fertile France, put up her lovely visage?
Alas, she hath from France too long been chased,
And all her husbandry doth lie on heaps,
Corrupting in its own fertility.   20
Her vine, the merry cheerer of the heart,
Unprunèd dies; her hedges even-pleached,
Like prisoners wildly overgrown with hair,
Put forth disordered twigs; her fallow leas
The darnel, hemlock, and rank fumitory
Doth root upon, while that the coulter rusts
That should deracinate such savagery.
The even mead, that erst brought sweetly forth
The freckled cowslip, burnet, and green clover,
Wanting the scythe, all uncorrected, rank,   30
Conceives by idleness, and nothing teems
But hateful docks, rough thistles, kecksies, burs,
Losing both beauty and utility;
And as our vineyards, fallows, meads, and hedges,
Defective in their natures, grow to wildness,
Even so our houses and ourselves and children
Have lost, or do not learn for want of time,
The sciences that should become our country,
But grow like savages–as soldiers will
That nothing do but meditate on blood–   40
To swearing and stern looks, diffused attire,
And everything that seems unnatural.
Which to reduce into our former favour
We are assembled; and my speech entreats
That I may know the let why gentle peace
Should not expel these inconveniences,
And bless us with her former qualities.
KING HENRY
    To cry 'Amen' to that, thus we appear.

But if, my gracious lord, you would that peace
Whose want gives growth to th'imperfections   50
Which you have cited, you must buy that peace
With full accord to all our just demands,
Whose tenors and particular effects
You have, enscheduled briefly, in your hands.

BURGUNDY
The King hath heard them, to the which as yet
There is no answer made.

KING HENRY   Well then, the peace
Which you before so urged lies in his answer.

FRENCH KING
I have but with a cursitory eye
O'erglanced the articles. Pleaseth your grace   60
To appoint some of your Council presently
To sit with us once more, with better heed
To re-survey them, we will suddenly
Pass our accept and peremptory answer.

KING HENRY
Brother, we shall. Go, uncle Exeter,
And brother Clarence, and you, brother Gloucester,
And cousin Westmoreland, go with the King.
And take with you free power to ratify,
Augment, or alter, as your wisdoms best
Shall see advantageable for our dignity,   70
Anything in or out of our demands,
And we'll consign thereto. Will you, fair sister,
Go with the Princes, or stay here with us?

QUEEN ISABEL
Our gracious brother, I will go with them.
Haply a woman's voice may do some good,
When articles too nicely urged be stood on.

KING HENRY
Yet leave our cousin Katherine here with us;
She is our capital demand, comprised
Within the fore-rank of our articles.

FRENCH KING
She hath good leave.
            Exeunt all but Henry, Katherine, and Alice

KING HENRY   Fair Katherine, and most fair,
Will you vouchsafe to teach a soldier terms
Such as will enter at a lady's ear
And plead his love-suit to her gentle heart?

KATHERINE
Your majesty shall mock at me; I cannot speak your
England.   80

KING HENRY
O fair Katherine, if you will love me soundly with
your French heart, I will be glad to hear you confess
it brokenly with your English tongue. Do you like
me, Kate?

KATHERINE
Pardonnez-moi, I cannot tell wat is 'like me'.

KING HENRY
An angel is like you, Kate, and you are like an angel.

KATHERINE
Que dit-il? que je suis semblable à un ange?

ALICE
Oui, vraiment, sauf votre grâce, ainsi dit-il.

KING HENRY
I said so, dear Katherine, and I must not blush to
affirm it.   90

KATHERINE
O mon Dieu! Les langues des hommes sont pleines
de tromperies.

KING HENRY
What says she, fair one? that the tongues of men are
full of deceits?

ALICE
Oui, dat de tongues of de mans is be full of deceits – dat
is de Princesse.

KING HENRY
The Princess is the better Englishwoman. I'faith, Kate,
my wooing is fit for thy understanding. I am glad
thou canst speak no better English; for if thou couldst,
thou wouldst find me such a plain king that thou   100
wouldst think I had sold my farm to buy my crown.
I know no ways to mince it in love, but directly to
say, 'I love you': then if you urge me farther than

to say, 'Do you, in faith?' I wear out my suit. Give
me your answer, i'faith, do; and so clap hands, and
a bargain. How say you, lady?

KATHERINE
Sauf votre honneur, me understand well.

KING HENRY
Marry, if you would put me to verses, or to dance
for your sake, Kate, why, you undid me. For the one,
I have neither words nor measure; and for the other,   110
I have no strength in measure, yet a reasonable
measure in strength. If I could win a lady at leapfrog,
or by vaulting into my saddle with my armour on
my back, under the correction of bragging be it spoken,
I should quickly leap into a wife. *Or if I might buffet
for my love, or bound my horse for her favours.* I could
lay on like a butcher, and sit like a jackanapes, never
off. But, before God, Kate, I cannot look greenly, nor
gasp out my eloquence, nor I have no cunning in
protestation: *only downright oaths, which I never use
till urged, nor never break for urging. If thou canst
love a fellow of this temper, Kate, whose face is not
worth sunburning, that never looks in his glass for love
of anything he sees there, let thine eye be thy cook.*
I speak to thee plain soldier. If thou canst love me
for this, take me; it not, to say to thee that I shall   120
die is true–but for thy love, by the Lord, no–yet I
love thee too. *And while thou liv'st, dear Kate, take
a fellow of plain and uncoined constancy; for he perforce
must do thee right, because he hath not the gift to woo
in other places. For these fellows of infinite tongue, that
can rhyme themselves into ladies' favours, they do always
reason themselves out again. What! A speaker is but
a prater, a rhyme is but a ballad. A good leg will fall;
a straight back will stoop; a black beard will turn
white; a curled pate will grow bald; a fair face will
wither; a full eye will wax hollow: but a good heart,*

115; 119 following; 122 following: The cuts here were not preconceived. In
rehearsal a natural rhythm emerged which precluded some lines; others are
purely repetitious. Every line could be argued back in. We found it a better
over-all balance without them.

Kate, is the sun and the moon—or rather, the sun, and
not the moon; for it shines bright and never changes,
but keeps his course truly. If thou would have such
a one, take me; and take me, take a soldier; take
a soldier, take a king. And what say'st thou then to
my love? Speak, my fair, and fairly, I pray thee.

KATHERINE
Is it possible dat I sould love de ennemi of France?

KING HENRY
No, it is not possible you should love the enemy of
France, Kate, but in loving me you should love the
friend of France, for I love France so well that I will   130
not part with a village of it—I will have it all mine:
and Kate, when France is mine, and I am yours, then
yours is France, and you are mine.

KATHERINE
I cannot tell wat is dat.

KING HENRY
No, Kate? I will tell thee in French, which I am sure
will hang upon my tongue like a new-married wife
about her husband's neck, hardly to be shook off.
Je—quand sur le possession de France, et quand vous
avez le possession de moi,—let me see, what then?
Saint Denis be my speed!—donc vôtre est France, et   140
vous êtes mienne. It is as easy for me, Kate, to conquer
the kingdom as to speak so much more French. I
shall never move thee in French, unless it be to laugh
at me.

KATHERINE
Sauf votre honneur, le français que vous parlez, il
est meilleur que l'anglais lequel je parle.

127 Is it possible dat I sould love de ennemi of France? Alan Howard (Henry):
I think at this point Henry realises Katherine's strength. Before this he
has tried to win her somewhat cursorily. When she says this he begins to
realise that he has literally, met his match.

Ludmila Mikaël (Katherine): I think this line changes the whole direction
of the scene. Before this, Katherine is charming, complaisant—a pretty girl.
At this point she asks Henry a particularly pertinent question. He gets out
of it very skilfully—but their relationship has changed. He needs skill, and
honesty, in dealing with her. She will not compromise with less. What had
been a political match or infatuation on both sides becomes something more.

KING HENRY
No, faith, is't not, Kate; but thy speaking of my tongue,
and I thine, most truly-falsely, must needs be granted
to be much at one. But Kate, dost thou understand
thus much English, Kate–canst thou love me?   150

KATHERINE
I cannot tell.

KING HENRY
Can any of your neighbours tell, Kate? I'll ask them.
Come, I know thou lovest me; and at night, when
you come into your closet, you'll question this
gentlewoman about me; and I know, Kate, you will
to her dispraise those parts in me that you love with
your heart. But, good Kate, mock me mercifully; the
rather, gentle Princess, because I love thee cruelly.
If ever thou beest mine, Kate, as I have a saving faith
within me tells me thou shalt, I get thee with scambling,   160
and thou must therefore needs prove a good
soldier-breeder. Shall not thou and I, between Saint
Denis and Saint George, compound a boy, half French,
half English, that shall go to Constantinople and take
the Turk by the beard? Shall we not? What say'st
thou, my fair flower-de-luce?

KATHERINE
I do not know dat.

KING HENRY
Non-'tis hereafter to know, but now to promise. Do
but now promise, Kate, you will endeavour for your
French part of such a boy, and for my English moiety   170
take the word of a king and a bachelor. How answer
you, la plus belle Katherine du monde, Ma très cher
et devin déesse?

KATHERINE
Oh, Your majestee 'ave fausse French enough to
deceive de most sage demoiselle dat is en France.

KING HENRY
Now fie upon my false French! By mine honour, in
true English, I love thee, Kate: by which honour I dare
not swear thou lovest me, yet my blood begins to
flatter me that thou dost, notwithstanding the poor and

untempering effect of my visage. Now beshrew my 180
father's ambition! He was thinking of civil wars when
he got me; therefore was I created with a stubborn
outside, with an aspect of iron, that when I come
to woo ladies I fright them. But in faith, Kate, the
elder I wax, the better I shall appear. My comfort
is, that old age, that ill layer-up of beauty, can do
no more spoil upon my face. Thou hast me, if thou
hast me, at the worst; and thou shalt wear me, if
thou wear me, better and better; and therefore tell
me, most fair Katherine, will you have me? *Put off* 190
your maiden blushes, avouch the thoughts of your heart
with the looks of an empress, take me by the hand,
and say, 'Harry of England, I am thine': which word
thou shalt no sooner bless mine ear withal but I will
tell thee aloud, 'England is thine, Ireland is thine, France
is thine, and Henry Plantagenet is thine'–who, though
I speak it before his face, if he be not fellow with the
best king, thou shalt find the best king of good fellows.
Come, your answer in broken music–for thy voice
is music, and thy English broken; therefore, Queen
of all, Katherine, *break thy mind to me in broken*
English–wilt thou have me?

KATHERINE
Dat is as it shall please de Roi mon père.

KING HENRY
Nay, it will please him well, Kate–it shall please him,
Kate.

KATHERINE
Den it sall also content me.

KING HENRY
Upon that I kiss your hand, and I call you my Queen.

KATHERINE
Laissez, mon seigneur, laissez, laissez! Ma foi, je ne
veux point que vous abaissiez votre grandeur en 200
baisant la main d'une–notre Seigneur–indigne
serviteur. Excusez-moi, je vous supplie, mon très
puissant seigneur.

KING HENRY
Then I will kiss your lips, Kate.

KATHERINE
> Les dames et demoiselles pour être baisées devant leurs noces, il n'est pas la coutume de France.

KING HENRY
> Madam my interpreter, what says she?

ALICE
> Dat it is not be de fashion pour les ladies of France – I cannot tell wat is baiser en Anglish.

KING HENRY
> To kiss.   210

ALICE
> Your majestee entendre bettre que moi.

KING HENRY
> It is not a fashion for the maids in France to kiss before they are married, would she say?

ALICE
> Oui, vraiment.

KING HENRY
> O Kate, nice customs curtsy to great kings. Dear Kate, you and I cannot be confined within the weak list of a country's fashion. We are the makers of manners, Kate, and the liberty that follows our places stops the mouth of all find-faults – as I will do yours for upholding the nice fashion of your country in denying   220 me a kiss; therefore, patiently, and yielding.
>
> (*He kisses her*)
>
> You have witchcraft in your lips, Kate: there is more eloquence in a sugar touch of them than in the tongues of the French Council, and they should sooner persuade Harry of England than a general petition of monarchs. Here comes your father.
>> *Enter the French King, Burgundy, and English and French Lords*

BURGUNDY
> *God save your majesty! My royal cousin,*
> *teach you our Princess English?*

226 following: the cuts here were forced upon us by the audience; the marriage has been agreed; soon we will all of us want to go home. And the rest of the scene, which is important, is held up by these courtly circumlocutions.

KING HENRY

I would have her learn, my fair cousin, how perfectly I love her, and that is good English.

BURGUNDY

Is she not apt?

KING HENRY

Our tongue is rough, coz, and my condition is not smooth; so that, having neither the voice nor the heart of flattery about me, I cannot so conjure up the spirit of love in her that he will appear in his true likeness.

BURGUNDY

Pardon the frankness of my mirth, if I answer you for that. If you would conjure in her, you must make a circle; if conjure up love in her in his true likeness, he must appear naked and blind. Can you blame her, then, being a maid yet rosed over with the virgin crimson of modesty, if she deny the appearance of a naked blind boy in her naked seeing self? It were, my lord, a hard condition for a maid to consign to.

KING HENRY

Yet they do wink and yield, as love is blind and enforces.

BURGUNDY

They are then excused, my lord, when they see not what they do.

KING HENRY

Then, good my lord, teach your cousin to consent winking.

BURGUNDY

I will wink on her to consent, my lord, if you will teach her to know my meaning: for maids, well summered and warm kept, are like flies at Bartholomewtide, blind, though they have their eyes, and then they will endure handling, which before would not abide looking on.

KING HENRY

This moral ties me over to time and a hot summer; and so I shall catch the fly, your cousin, in the latter end, and she must be blind too.

BURGUNDY

As love is, my lord, before it loves.

KING HENRY

*It is so; and you may, some of you, thank love for my
blindness, who cannot see many a fair French city for
one fair French maid that stands in my way.*

FRENCH KING

*Yes, my lord, you see them perspectively, the cities turned
into a maid; for they are all girdled with maiden walls,
that war hath never entered.*

KING HENRY

Shall Kate be my wife?

FRENCH KING

So please you.

KING HENRY

*I am content, so the maiden cities you talk of may wait
on her: so the maid that stood in the way for my wish
shall show me the way to my will.*

FRENCH KING

We have consented to all terms of reason.

KING HENRY

Is't so, my lords of England?

WESTMORELAND

The King hath granted every article:
His daughter first, and then, in sequel, all,   230
According to their firm proposèd natures.

EXETER

Only he hath not yet subscribèd this:
Where your majesty demands that the King of France,
having any occasion to write for matter of grant, shall
name your highness in this form, and with this
addition, in French, Notre très cher fils Henri, Roi
d'Angleterre, Héritier de France: and thus in Latin,
Praeclarissimus filius noster Henricus, Rex Angliae
et Haeres Franciae.

FRENCH KING

Nor this I have not, brother, so denied   240
But your request shall make us let it pass.

236 It is interesting that Henry, whose obsession with his own father, and
with surrogate fathers like Falstaff and the Lord Chief Justice in the earlier
plays, is so strong, should now at the very end of *Henry V* demand again
that he be accepted as a son.

KING HENRY
I pray you then, in love and dear alliance,
Let that one article rank with the rest,
And thereupon give me your daughter.

FRENCH KING
Take her, fair son, and from her blood raise up
Issue to me, that the contending kingdoms
Of France and England, whose very shores look pale
With envy of each other's happiness,
May cease their hatred, and this dear conjunction
Plant neighbourhood and Christian-like accord   250
In their sweet bosoms, that never war advance
His bleeding sword 'twixt England and fair France.

KING HENRY
Now welcome, Kate; and bear me witness all
That here I kiss her as my sovereign Queen.
God, the best maker of all marriages,
Combine our hearts in one, our realms in one!
As man and wife, being two, are one in love,
So be there 'twixt our kingdoms such a spousal
That never may ill office, or fell jealousy,
Which troubles oft the bed of blessèd marriage,   260
Thrust in between the paction of these kingdoms
To make divorce of their incorporate league;
That English may as French, French Englishmen,
Receive each other, God speak this 'Amen'!

ALL
Amen!

KING HENRY
Prepare we for our marriage; on which day,
My Lord of Burgundy, we'll take your oath,
And all the peers', for surety of our leagues.
Then shall I swear to Kate, and you to me,
And may our oaths well kept and prosperous be!
    The French and the English, led by Henry and
    Katherine, gradually join together in a group

255–264 God the best maker… The lines Henry speaks here are Queen Isabel's
in Shakespeare's text. The 'your' of 'your realms' and 'your kingdoms' has
been changed to 'our.'

*upstage. Burgundy (the Chorus) comes forward to
the audience.*

CHORUS

Thus far, with rough and all-unable pen,
  Our bending author hath pursued the story,
In little room confining mighty men,
  Mangling by starts the full course of their glory.
Small time, but in that small most greatly lived
  This star of England. Fortune made his sword,
By which the world's best garden he achieved,
  And of it left his son imperial lord.
Henry the Sixth, in infant bands crowned King
  Of France and England, did this King succeed,   10
Whose state so many had the managing
  That they lost France, and made his England bleed:
Which oft our stage hath shown; and, for their sake,
In your fair minds let this acceptance take.

1–14 Chorus: The play ends with a sonnet. It concludes and qualifies the evening. Like *A Midsummer Night's Dream*, the play ends with a joyful marriage, followed by a sad epitaph. Puck's reminder that 'Now the hungry lion roars' is akin to the Chorus' reminder of the fate of the boy compounded by Henry and Katherine–the boy who was to 'take the Turk by the beard'.

We have seen the Hal of the previous 'Henry' plays become King at great cost, both to others, and to himself. He has gone through a war which, whether waged rightly or wrongly, has changed him, and the men who fought with him. He achieves peace and a wife; there is the promise of constancy and a child. Yet he breeds future dissension, future desolation.

The plays runs hot and cold, and so ends. Its ambiguity is constant.

BIOGRAPHIES OF THE COMPANY, STRATFORD-UPON-AVON 1975

Peter Bourke

Francis in *Henry IV Part One, Part Two;* Boy in *Henry V.*
Work outside RSC includes: Four seasons with National
Youth Theatre. Member of the Interaction team (1969). Claudio
in *Measure for Measure*, Camille in *A Flea in her Ear*, Young
Fashion in *The Relapse* (all Leeds 1972/73), King Edward
in *Richard III, Canterbury Tales, The Lovers*, and Happy
in *Death of a Salesman* (Leeds 1973/74). TV includes: *Initiation*
(Centre Play), *America America*, Tommy Traddles in *David
Copperfield* (1974).

Philip Brack

Sir Walter Blunt in *Henry IV Part One;* Lord Bardolph in
Henry IV Part Two; Exeter in *Henry V.*
Work with RSC includes: Seasons with the company 1962–6
including *Macbeth, Lear* (1962), *Julius Caesar, Comedy of
Errors* (1968), Exton in *Richard II*, Constable in *Henry V*,
Duke of Somerset in *Wars of the Roses* trilogy (1964), Corporal
in *Don't Make Me Laugh*, Sir Percival Smoothely Smooth
in *The Thwarting of Baron Bollingrew* (Aldwych 1965).
Work outside RSC includes: Father Griffin in *Child's Play*
(Queens), films include *A Man for All Seasons* (1966). *The
Darwin Adventure* (1972). Many T.V. appearances including
Hamlet, King Lear, Richie McLeod in *United* (1967), Det.
Insp. James Cook in *Softly Softly* (1967/8), *The Main Chance*
(1975).

Bernard Brown

Vernon in *Henry IV Part One;* Travers in *Henry IV Part Two;*
Constable of France in *Henry V.*
Work outside RSC includes: Title role in *Hamlet* (Baalbek
Festival, Lebanon 1956), Pip in *Great Expectations* (Bristol
Old Vic 1957), Hal in *Henry IV Part One, Part Two;* (tour
of England and Scotland 1958), Petruchio in *The Taming
of the Shrew* (Regents Park 1958), The Interrogator in *The
Prisoner* (Oxford Playhouse and Cambridge 1962). Season

233

with Belgrade, Coventry (1962/63) including Don Pedro in *Much Ado about Nothing*. Macready in *Robert and Elizabeth* (Lyric 1965), Teddy in *The Homecoming* (Oxford 1966), Maurice Duclos in *Fallen Angels* (Vaudeville 1967), 1968/70 toured S Africa in a variety of roles including Richard II, Falstaff, Othello. Directed *Macbeth* (Cape Town 1972). Many TV appearances include: *The Regiment* (1972/73), *The Pallisers* (1973/74), *Nightingale's Boys* (1975).

Yvonne Coulette
Lady Northumberland in *Henry IV Part Two;* Alice in *Henry V.*
Work outside RSC includes: Seasons with Nottingham Playhouse (1965), and Bristol Old Vic (1966). Has appeared in five British Council tours over the past 10 years. Lysistrata in *The Apple Cart* (Mermaid Theatre 1970), Queen Mary in *Crown Matrimonial* (Thorndike Theatre 1974), Sheila Boothroyd in *Lloyd George Knew My Father*, Joanna in *Games* (both Leicester 1975). TV includes: *Daniel Deronda*, *Middlemarch*, Mrs Arnold in *Tom Brown's School Days*, *Spy Trap* (1974).

Richard Derrington
Drawer in *Henry IV Part One;* Court in *Henry V*, Shadow in *Henry IV Part Two*.
Work outside RSC includes: Biondello in *The Taming of the Shrew*, Larry in *The Boys in the Band* (Salisbury 1971), Claire in *The Maids*, George Arthur Rose in *Hadrian VII* (Salisbury 1972), Danny in *Night Must Fall* (Nairobi 1973), Pseudocus in *A Funny Thing Happened on the Way to the Forum* (St Andrews 1974).

Philip Dunbar
Nym and Orleans in *Henry V;* Nym in *The Merry Wives of Windsor*, *The Mouth Organ* (The Other Place).
Work with RSC includes: Ross in *Richard II* (Stratford and Aldwych 1974), Stark in *Comrades*, Nuttall in *The Beast* (both The Place 1974), Roman Captain in *Cymbeline*, Bigot in *King John* (both Aldwych 1975).
Work outside RSC includes: Brutus in *Julius Caesar*, Don John in *Much Ado About Nothing* (Newcastle 1967/68),

Lodovico in *Othello* (Oxford 1971), Pistol in *Henry V* (Farnham 1973), Richard in *The Lion in Winter*, Lucius O'Trigger in *The Rivals* (Harrogate 1973), *A Man for all Seasons* (film 1966). TV includes: *Country Matters* (1972), *Six Days of Justice* (1973).

Farrah
Designs *Henry IV Part One, Part Two;* and *Henry V.*
Work with RSC includes: *The Tempest* (1963), *The Cherry Orchard, Curtmantle, Puntila, Dr Faustus* (1968), *Richard III, The Plebeians, The Duchess of Malfi, The Balcony, Murder in the Cathedral, Romeo and Juliet, Taming of the Shrew, The Bewitched.*
Work outside RSC includes: *Don Giovanni* (Strasbourg 1960), Oedipus Rex (Sadler's Wells 1960), *The Dragon* (London 1967/68): ran the design course at the National Theatre of Canada (1969), designed Terry Hands' Comédie Française production of *Richard III*, and Clifford Williams' New York production of Pirandello's *Henry IV.*

Oliver Ford-Davies
Sherriff, Sir Michael, Traveller in *Henry IV Part One;* Morton, Wart in *Henry IV Part Two;* Montjoy, Governor of Harfleur in *Henry V.*
Work outside RSC includes: Left academic life for the stage in 1967. Played Gaunt in *Richard II* (Birmingham Rep 1967), Bishop of Caerleon in *Hadrian VII* (London 1968), Col. Pickering in *Pygmalion* (Birmingham and Chicago 1970), Friar Laurence in *Romeo and Juliet* (Oxford Playhouse 1972), Mr Moreland in *Mary Rose* (London 1972). Season with Cambridge Theatre Company (1973) where parts included: Horatio in *Hamlet*, and Sir Peter Teazle in *School for Scandal.* TV includes: *Father Brown, The Brontes of Haworth* (1974). Has written plays for TV and the London fringe, and directed at Birmingham and Leicester.

Terry Hands
Directs *Henry IV Part One, Part Two; Henry V* and *The Merry Wives of Windsor.*
Work with RSC includes: Artistic director Theatregoround 1966/68, directed *The Criminals, The Merry Wives of Windsor,*

Pericles, Bartholomew Fair, Women Beware Women, Pleasure and Repentance (Theatregoround), *Richard III, The Balcony, The Man of Mode, The Merchant of Venice, Murder in the Cathedral, Romeo and Juliet, The Bewitched.*

Work outside RSC includes: Founder director of Liverpool Everyman Theatre, directed *The Great God Brown, Murder in the Cathedral, The Four Seasons, Orison, Fando and Lis* (all Liverpool 1964/66), *Richard III* at the Comédie Française (also seen in London in the World Theatre Season), *Pericles* (Comédie Française).

Alan Howard

Prince Hal in *Henry IV Part One, Part Two; Henry V.*

Work with RSC includes: Orsino in *Twelfth Night* (1966), Lussurioso in *Revenger's Tragedy* (1966/67/69), Jaques in *As You Like It* (1967), Edgar in *King Lear*, Benedick in *Much Ado About Nothing*, Achilles in *Troilus and Cressida* (all 1968), Hamlet, Mephistophilis in *Dr Faustus* (both 1970), Oberon/Theseus in *A Midsummer Night's Dream* (1970/73 and World Tour), Dorimant in *Man of Mode, Enemies, The Balcony* (all Aldwych 1971), Carlos II in Peter Barnes' *The Bewitched* (Aldwych 1974).

Work outside RSC includes: Belgrade, Coventry (1958/60), Wesker Trilogy (Coventry and Royal Court 1959/60), 1st Chichester season 1961, Angelo in *Measure for Measure* and Bolingbroke in *Richard II* (both Nottingham 1965), Handke's *Ride Across Lake Constance* and Cyril in C. P. Taylor's *The Black and White Minstrels* (both Hampstead Theatre Club 1974). Most recent TV appearances: Fred Banting in *Banting and Best* (1974), and Mirabell in *The Way of the World* (1975).

Geoffrey Hutchings

Dauphin in *Henry V;* Simple in *The Merry Wives of Windsor, The Mouth Organ* (The Other Place).

Work with RSC includes: Octavius Caesar in *Julius Caesar* (1969), Cromwell in *Henry VIII* (1969), Bosola in *Duchess of Malfi* (1971), Dromio of Syracuse in *Comedy of Errors*, Clown in *Antony and Cleopatra* (1972), Jasper in *Section 9* (Place 1973).

Work outside RSC includes: Work with Nottingham Playhouse and Liverpool Everyman. Recent work includes

King Arthur in *The King* (Shaw 1974), Gangster in *Kiss me Kate* (Oxford Playhouse 1974). TV includes: *A Little Bit of Wisdom* (1974), *Clayhanger.*

Emrys James
Henry IV; Chorus in *Henry V;* Evans in *The Merry Wives of Windsor.*
Work with RSC includes: Gower in *Pericles* (1969), The Boss in *The Plebeians* (Aldwych 1971), Feste in *Twelfth Night* (1969), The Cardinal in *The Duchess of Malfi* (1971), Iago in *Othello* (1971), Shylock in *The Merchant of Venice* (1971), Merlin in *Island of the Mighty* (Aldwych 1972), title role in *King John* (Stratford 1974, Aldwych 1975), Mephistophilis in *Dr Faustus* (Aldwych and tour 1974).
Work outside RSC includes: Private Evans in *The Long and the Short and the Tall* (London 1959). Caesar/Octavius in *Julius Caesar*, Richmond in *Richard III*, Malcolm in *Macbeth* (Old Vic 1962), Juryman No. 9 in *Twelve Angry Men* (London 1964). Has appeared in many TV plays including recently Doolittle in *Pygmalion*, Lloyd George in *Wipers Three*, Sir Toby Belch in *Twelfth Night*, and Dr Pangloss in *Candide* (1974), and TV series including *Softly Softly*, *Wessex Tales* (1973), *Fall of Eagles* (1974), and *Days of Hope* (1975).

Stephen Jenn
Humphrey of Gloucester in *Henry IV Part One*, *Part Two;* and *Henry V.*
Work outside RSC includes: Seasons with Chichester Festival Theatre (1969) and with Birmingham Rep where parts included Chorus in *Oedipus*, Francois Dauphin in *Vivat Vivat Regina* (1972), Yepihodov in *The Cherry Orchard*, Silvio in *Servant of Two Masters* (Theatre Royal York 1972). Silvius in *As You Like It*, Valentine in *Twelfth Night* (Regents Park 1973), Clarence in *Richard III* (York 1973), Narrator in *The Soldier's Tale*, Ninian Fraser in *First Mrs Fraser* (York 1974).

Reginald Jessup
Westmoreland in *Henry IV Part One, Part Two;* and *Henry V.*
Work outside RSC includes: Judge Brack in *Hedda Gabler* (Cardiff 1967), *Glendower in Henry IV Part One* (Billingham

1971), Tom in *Treasure Island* (Mermaid 1973), Rudi in *Romeo loves Juliet* (Chichester 1973), Neville Chamberlain in *The Thingamybob*, The Colonel in Planchon's *Blues Whites and Reds* (both Birmingham Rep 1974), Councillor Higgins in *Coming of Age* (Octagon Bolton 1974). TV includes: *Gideon's Way* (1965). After a pools win in the 1950s, started his own company presenting plays to children in London schools.

Ian Judge
Assistant to the director.
Work outside RSC includes: as an actor, seasons at Worthing (1971), Nottingham Playhouse (1972), Crewe (1973). Rabbit in *Winnie the Pooh* (Phoenix Theatre and tour 1974). TV includes: *Warship*, *Doctor in charge* and *No Honestly*. Studied at the Guildhall School where he directed *The Marowitz Hamlet*. Directed *The Dumb Waiter* (Worthing 1972), *The Valkyrie* (opera, London 1974).

Clement McCallin
Northumberland in *Henry IV Part One, Part Two;* King of France in *Henry V*.
Work with RSC includes: The Duke in *The Two Gentlemen of Verona* (1969), First Player in *Hamlet* (1970), Lucifer in *Doctor Faustus* (Theatregoround 1970), Police Inspector in *Enemies* (Aldwych 1971), Judge in *The Balcony* (Aldwych 1971), Cominius Messala and Agrippa in *The Romans* (1972), Escalus/Chorus in *Romeo and Juliet* (1973), Northumberland in *Richard II* (1973), Duke Frederick in *As You Like It* (1973), King of France in *King John* (Stratford 1974, Aldwych 1975), Northumberland/John of Gaunt in *Richard II* (1974), Lucifer in *Doctor Faustus* (Aldwych 1974 and tour).
Work outside RSC includes: *Henry V* (Stratford 1936, TV 1950), Gayev in *The Cherry Orchard* (Pitlochry 1966), Esteban Zoltan in *Happy Deathday* (London 1967, film 1968). Married to actress Brenda Bruce.

Dan Meaden
Douglas in *Henry IV Part One;* Hastings in *Henry IV Part Two;* Scroop and Williams in *Henry V;* Host in *The Merry Wives of Windsor*.
Work with RSC includes: Mistress Overdone/Barnadine/

Francisca in *Measure for Measure*, Alonso in *The Tempest* (1974).
Work outside RSC includes: Tiger Brown in *The Threepenny Opera* (London 1972), *Antony and Cleopatra* (London 1973), *Great Society* (Mermaid 1974). TV includes: Detective Box in *Softly Softly* (1970/72), *The Jensen Code* (1972), *Nine Tailors* (1973), *Boy Dominic* (1974).

Ludmila Mikaël
Katherine in *Henry V.* Trained at the Paris Conservatoire. Pensionaire at the Comédie Française 1967–1974. Sociétaire, Comédie Française since 1974. Parts there include Elvire in Moliere's *Don Juan;* Lumir in Claudel's *Le Pain Dur;* Lady Anne in Terry Hands' Paris production of *Richard III;* Thaisa/Marina in *Pericles;* she is currently appearing as Yse in Claudel's *Partage du Midi* at the Comédie Française, and preparing Viola for Terry Hands' production of *Twelfth Night* there in early 1976.

Richard Moore
Pistol in *Henry IV Part Two, Henry V* and *The Merry Wives of Windsor.*
Work with RSC includes: Guildenstern in *Hamlet* (Stratford 1965), Pistol in *Henry IV Part Two;* and *Henry V* (Stratford 1966), Ajax in *Troilus and Cressida*, Wagner in *Dr Faustus* (both Stratford 1968). Harry Heegan in *The Silver Tassie* (Aldwych 1969), Starvling in *A Midsummer Night's Dream* (World Tour 1972/73). Extensive work with Theatregoround including Estragon in *Waiting for Godot* and Narrator in *Under Milk Wood.*
Work outside RSC includes: Mitchem in *The Long and the Short and the Tall* (Shaw 1972), Banquo in *Macbeth* (Shaw 1973), Benedick in *Much Ado About Nothing* (Leicester 1973), Petruchio in *The Taming of the Shrew* (Cheltenham 1973), title role in *Hans Kohlhaas* (Greenwich 1973). Films include: *Raging Moon* (1970). *The Offence* (1972), *Juggernaut* (1974). TV includes: *The Guardians, Big Soft Nelly.*

Anthony Naylor
Thomas, Duke of Clarence in *Henry IV Part One, Part Two;* and *Henry V.*

Work outside RSC includes: Seasons with Leeds Playhouse (1972), and Crucible Sheffield (1973), Freddy in *Pygmalion* (Albery 1974). Films include: *The Lovers* (1972), *Penny Gold* (1973), *Stardust* (1974). TV includes: *So It Goes* (1973), *Z Cars* (1973).

Trevor Peacock

Poins in *Henry IV Part One;* Poins and Silence in *Henry IV Part Two;* Fluellen in *Henry V.*
Work with RSC includes: Prince in *Sherlock Holmes* (Aldwych and New York 1974), Duro and Tenda in *The Bewitched* (Aldwych 1974).
Work outside RSC includes: Began his career as a comedian at The Windmill (1956). *Hamlet* (Edinburgh 1968), Tony Lumpkin in *She Stoops to Conquer* (Garrick 1969), Kite in *The Recruiting Officer* (Cambridge 1970), Bloody Five Shot in *Man is Man* (Royal Court 1971), title role in *Titus Andronicus* (Roundhouse 1971), Clov in *Endgame* (Shaw 1969), Sir John Brute in *The Provok'd Wife* (Watford 1972), Petruchio in *The Taming of the Shrew* (Young Vic 1972). *Lady Caroline Lamb* (film 1974). TV includes: *She Stoops to Conquer* (1972), *Edward G—Like the Film Star* (1973). Also playwright and songwriter, work includes various TV plays, *Collapse of a Stout Party, Who Rides a Tiger* (film). His *Three Men Went to War* is to be filmed later this year.

Maureen Pryor

Mistress Quickly in *Henry IV Part One, Part Two; Henry V* and *The Merry Wives of Windsor.*
Work outside RSC includes: Bertha in *Boeing Boeing* (New York 1965), Muriel in *After the Rain* (London and New York 1965), a season with Bristol Old Vic (1968), Nurse in *Romeo and Juliet* (Regents Park 1971), Athol Fugard's *People are Living Here* (King's Head 1971). The wife in *Edward G—Like the Film Star* (King's Head 1972), The wife in *All Over* (York 1973). Films include: *The Music Lovers, Caroline Lamb, National Health*. Many TV appearances include: *Song of Summer, Family Reunion, Fenn Street Gang, Caucasian Chalk Circle, Shoulder to Shoulder*.

Carolle Rousseau
Katherine in *Henry V.*
Work outside RSC includes: Trained for the theatre in Belgium and France. Worked in French TV and with a troop of actors in Paris on classical texts, touring to North Africa. Work in England includes: Helen in *Soft Beds and Hard Battles* (film 1973).

Barrie Rutter
Chamberlain in *Henry IV;* Cambridge and Macmorris in *Henry V.*
Work outside RSC includes: Eleven years with the National Youth Theatre for which he has directed *Fuzz, Spring-heeled Jack, Good Lads at Heart,* and *Geordies' March,* all by Peter Terson. Grumio in *The Taming of the Shrew* (Shaw 1974). TV includes: *Queenie's Castle* (1971/73).

Derek Smith
Canterbury and Gower in *Henry V;* Dr Caius in *The Merry Wives of Windsor.*
Work with RSC includes: Talbot/Cade in *The Wars of the Roses,* Stephano in *The Tempest* (1963), Dad in *Little Murders* (1967), Dr Caius in *The Merry Wives of Windsor* (1968), Autolycus in *The Winter's Tale* (1969), Simonides in *Pericles* (1969), Meddle in *London Assurance* (Aldwych 1970), Touchstone in *As You Like It,* Holofernes in *Love's Labour's Lost,* Baptista in *The Taming of the Shrew* (1973).
Work outside RSC includes: Pierre in *War and Peace,* title role in musical *Fiorello* (both Bristol and London 1962), The Professor in *Incident at Vichy* (London 1966), title role in *Toad of Toad Hall* (London 1967, 1971, Stratford 1973), Fluther Good in *The Plough and the Stars* (Canada 1974), *Alfie Darling* (film 1975). TV includes: *Forsyte Saga* (1966), *The Guardians* (1971), *Black Beauty* (1973), *Shades of Green* (1975).

Ken Stott
Ralph in *Henry IV, Part One;* Gower, Ralph in *Henry IV, Part Two;* Jamy in *Henry V.*
Work outside RSC includes: Dunois in *St. Joan,* Angus in *Macbeth,* Judas in *Jesus Christ Superstar* (all Lyric Belfast

1973/74), Pharaoh in *Joseph and His Amazing Technicolour Dreamcoat* (Newcastle 1974), Yasha in *The Cherry Orchard* (TV 1972). Has also sung with "Still Life" jazz and mime group (1973).

Arthur Whybrow
Gadshill in *Henry IV Part One;* Servant, Fang, Feeble, Beadle in *Henry IV Part Two;* Bates in *Henry V.*
Work with RSC includes: *The Romans* (1972).
Work outside RSC includes: Seasons with many repertory theatres, Long John Silver in *Treasure Island* (Lincoln 1965), title role in *Othello* (Stoke 1969). Fitzpatrick in *The Contractor*, Dadda in *Entertaining Mr Sloane* (both Belgrade Coventry 1971). TV includes: *The Time of Your Life* (1971), *The Love-girl and the Innocent, Six Days of Justice* (both 1973), *General Hospital* (1974), *Goodbye* (Play for Today 1975), *Dixon of Dock Green* (1975).

Guy Woolfenden
Composer for *Henry IV Part One, Part Two; Henry V* and *The Merry Wives of Windsor.*
Work with RSC includes: As music director has composed scores for over 50 productions including every Shakespeare play except *Cymbeline, The Comedy of Errors* and *The Two Gentlemen of Verona* – has made two records of his RSC music.
Work outside RSC includes: Principal conductor Liverpool Mozart Orchestra, Morley College Symphony Orchestra, and Warwickshire Symphony Orchestra, and has made guest appearances with the Winnipeg Symphony Orchestra and the Royal Philharmonic Orchestra; assistant director of *Moses and Aaron* (Covent Garden 1965). Has written music for the Chamber of Horrors at Madame Tussauds, feature films, many TV plays (including the RSC's *Antony and Cleopatra*), a musical: *What a Way to Run a Revolution!* and Terry Hands's productions of *Richard III* and *Pericles* at the Comédie Française.

Tim Wylton
Bardolph in *Henry IV Part One, Part Two;* Bardolph and Monseur Le Fer in *Henry V* and Bardolph in *The Merry Wives of Windsor.*

Work with RSC includes: Costard in *Love's Labour's Lost* (Stratford 1964), Friar Jacomo in *The Jew of Malta* (Stratford 1965), Bardolph in *Henry IV Part One, Part Two;* and *Henry V* (Stratford 1966), Hortensio in *The Taming of the Shrew* (Stratford 1967), Lory in *The Relapse* (Aldwych 1967), Bobchinsky in *The Government Inspector* (Aldwych 1965).

Work outside RSC includes: Mick in *Straight Up* (Piccadilly 1971), Hubert in *Country Life* (Hampstead 1973). Films include: *Swalk* (1971), *Under Milk Wood* (1972). Much TV work including: *The Liver Birds, Harry Worth, Her Majesty's Pleasure*, and Eric in the series *The Dustbin Men*.

AFTERWORD

RONALD BRYDEN

Someone asked Edmund Kean why he seemed so indifferent to the hysterical adulation of London audiences during his first triumphant season at Drury Lane. 'I have often acted the third act of Othello in the same manner as now calls down such thunders,' he answered, 'when the whole house laughed. After that, can you think that I care much for public taste?' Theatre people measure their work by their own private, professional standards, a good deal more rigorous than those of critics or public. Popular success, though pleasant, is fairly irrelevant to their own judgment of how they succeeded in their own terms. Publicly, the 1975 centennial season at Stratford was one of the most successful in the RSC's history. How did it look to the company privately? How successful was it in achieving our own aims and intentions?

It is too early yet to give a complete answer. Part of the season's intention was to present Shakespeare's '*Henry*' plays in a certain manner. In that, with some inevitable shortfalls and miscalculations, we think we achieved a fair degree of success. The other part of our intention was to persuade audiences to accept this new manner of presentation; to change their expectations and taste in the matter of staging Shakespeare. In this we appear both to have succeeded and failed. On the whole critics and audiences seemed to go along with the new style of presentation while they were in the theatre. They then went off and praised us for the opposite of what we set out to do, criticising us in the margins for achieving what we had intended.

Let me explain. A decade ago, when the histories were last performed at Stratford to celebrate Shakespeare's quatercentenary, Peter Hall and his team used them to make a partial revolution in Shakespearian staging. By painting out the sharp frame of the proscenium, thrusting the stage forward and playing scene after scene in vivid cross- and overhead lighting against John Bury's monochrome, massively-textured and emblematic sets, they turned the plays from the traditional historical frescoes into living sculpture. No attempt was made to paint a literal picture of fifteenth century England. What mattered was her people: solitary kings meditating in pools of candlelight during the dark hours of anxious nights; knots of courtiers whispering in half-shadows; phalanxes of armed men advancing frontally to the footlights. The plays, they demonstrated, could exist without literal settings: without the usual laborious shufflings of towers, battlements, portcullises and inglenooks. Freed from naturalistic concerns of place and time, in fact, they were released into new, dynamic life.

The 1964 history cycle was a half-way house between the traditional pictorial staging of Shakespeare and the possibility of a return to a fully authentic, anti-naturalistic Elizabethan staging. It covered half the distance between two distinct, diametrically opposed kinds of theatre: the theatre of illusion and the theatre of convention. Ten years later, it seemed time to go all the way: to see if it were possible once more to re-create a theatre which takes place not before the eyes of an audience, but within its head.

The theatre of illusion is a theatre of alternative reality. It asks its audience to forsake the reality they inhabit and enter another, giving their full belief to the staged appearance they will see. The theatre of convention is both more primitive and more sophisticated. It is the theatre of childhood: of the circle of jagged paper which is accepted as a royal crown, the two steps across a playground which become a day's march of armies. It is the simpler of the two yet infinitely more difficult. For it requires the audience to work with the actors, using its imagination as strenuously as children do in play. Above all, it requires today the overthrow of more than a century of aesthetic habit and expectation: a total break with the nineteenth century theatre of spectacle and verisimilitude. The first is already dying a natural death by cost inflation – Henry Irving's 'painting with gaslight' survives only in opera and musical comedy. But the second – Stanislavsky's achingly real theatre of bourgeois psychology and domestic life – is still the prevailing language of our majority drama. If breaking the habit of it is difficult for audiences, it is doubly difficult for actors. For they have to persuade each audience they play to into the forgotten mode of childhood. A convention is an agreement. The theatre of convention can only work if audiences as well as actors accept its idiom of make-believe.

Between the 1964 cycle of histories and 1975, the RSC travelled a long way down the road to such a theatre. There were seasons of bare white box-stages, productions in modern and semi-modern dress. Most important of all, there was in 1969 Peter Brook's *A Midsummer Night's Dream*, which turned the enchanted wood near Athens into a white circus-ring of tumbling acrobats and juggling tricks. It was the nearest thing to pure theatre-of-convention, the theatre of Noh and old Greek comedy, seen in this century. But it started from a comedy of fantasy, and even it relied to some extent on an alternative reality–a visual world of Persian folk-acting and echoes of Picasso's circus paintings. It still remained to test whether audiences would accept one of Shakespeare's 'realistic' plays–his histories or major tragedies–without any illusion at all, couched wholly in the language of Elizabethan stagecraft.

John Barton's *Richard II* in 1972, with its alternating player-kings donning stage-robes over their Jacobean tunics, pushed the frontier of convention a large step further. But again, it had the advantage of a highly formal, stylised text to start from: *Richard II* is generally recognised as one of Shakespeare's most artificial plays. Would audiences accept the conventional techniques which slipped so easily on to its patterned rhetoric in the later history plays, so long regarded as his most naturalistic? Would they agree to the artifice which had seemed an appropriate enough expression for a play about a king obviously both an actor and a poet if it were applied to Prince Hal and his Eastcheap companions, Falstaff, Bardolph, Nym and Pistol?

It really boiled down to a question of whether they would accept *Henry V.* Would they acquiesce in a production which took at their literal face value the Chorus speeches of the play in which Shakespeare stated most clearly the kind of staging he envisaged for his creations?

> *O, pardon! Since a crooked figure may*
> *Attest in little place a million;*

And let us, ciphers to this great accompt,
On your imaginary forces work…
Piece out our imperfections with your thoughts,
Into a thousand parts divide one man
And make imaginary puissance;
Think when we talk of horses that you see them
Printing their proud hoofs i'th'receiving earth;
For 'tis your thoughts that now must deck our kings.

There were cogent financial arguments for letting *Henry V*, always one of Shakespeare's most popular plays at British box offices, launch the 1975 cycle of histories out of proper chronology. It would fill the theatre in Straford single-handed for the weeks necessary to mount the heavier, more complex *Henry IV, Part One*. But the real reason why Terry Hands made it the first play of his season was that he wished the whole cycle to start from that bald, magnificent statement of intent. If audiences would accept the convention of actors in modern dress informing them that they were actors, not dead mediaeval worthies, about to tell the tale of Agincourt without illusion, it might be possible to play *Henry IV, Parts One* and *Two* as Shakespeare wrote them to be performed. If spectators could be made to recognise the greatest, most coherent description of a theatre of convention for what it was, the revolution begun in 1964 might be completed.

Was it? As I say, the evidence is conflicting. It is too early yet to say. Almost to a man, the critics of *Henry V* denounced the modern-dress Chorus and opening scene as boring and unnecessary. Yet almost to a man, they accepted the conventions of the rest of the production and hailed it as brilliantly successful. 'This,' wrote B. A. Young in the *Financial Times*, 'is what Shakespearian theatre must have been like if it ever attained the professional standards of the RSC.' Yet praise of the production seemed to focus on its elements of spectacle: the vivid pictorial effect of groupings on the huge, bare stage; the surprise of Farrah's canopies exploding with colour, or sagging to produce the illusion of a mud-coloured trenchscape. Illusion, after all, seemed to be what the determined reviewers insisted on deriving and taking away from their evening.

Perhaps that means the revolution succeeded to some

extent. The frontier between convention and illusion is hard to draw – is not the agreement to suspend disbelief and take a three-walled drawing-room for the real thing a convention too? Perhaps the critics played the game of imagination with the actors so well that they went away believing they had seen the traditional historical pageant. From the company's point of view, there was a kind of wry comfort to be drawn from the repeated descriptions of one of the most experimental, complex and difficult productions it had ever staged as simple, straightforward and ungimmicky. That *is* the effect of Elizabethan staging. The extraordinary task of recreating it in a modern, illusion-bred theatre, persuading audiences to accept it as the most natural style in the world, went unnoticed. That was victory of a kind.

The victory belonged to the actors – on that the company and its critics can agree. There are various practical advantages to a theatre of convention. It is quicker, it is cheaper, it is more flexible than the theatre of illusion. It can bring the unseen on to the stage in a way pictorial theatre never can. But the main reason for struggling to re-establish it as our mode of playing Shakespeare is that it frees the actor, putting back on his shoulders the heroic task of conjuring from the audience the vision the stage denies. In a theatre of convention, he is no longer merely an interpreter. He is a creator, *the* creator. What success *Henry V* had from the private, professional point of view which matters most to the theatre and its people, its actors created. Judging their own work, they can be satisfied.

THE TIMES

CHARLES LEWSEN

Henry V stands as a work in its own right more than either of the two parts of *Henry IV*, yet it seems unfair both to the production of Terry Hands and the Henry of Alan Howard that, due to the greater popularity of the patriotic tub-thumping third play, we should be shown it before its predecessors...

Rehearsal and performance of the *Henry IV* plays will no doubt modify the present production. Nevertheless some clear lines have been laid down. Two assumptions of regal costume –the first, with awe and terror as he takes up the Dauphin's challenge and prepares for battle in France, the second with easy confidence after he has been bloodied and before the battle of Agincourt–show that Mr Howard does not regard the putting aside of Falstaff as Hal's last step to maturity.

Indeed, mention of Falstaff and of Bardolph's theft still have power to bring tears to the vulnerable eyes of this Henry, as does the sense of guilt for his father's overthrow of Richard II; and the whole foundation of this intelligent performance is of a man's attempt to forge himself in the painful fires of authority and battle. Witnessing a man's growth last night even caused me to wish that there was a fourth play to take Mr Howard's Henry beyond even the wooing of Katherine.

Design of the *Henry* plays is in the hands of Farrah. I take it the bare platform, bounded on two sides by a high balcony and backed by a white brick wall, will serve throughout. That being so, it is safe to assume that in the earlier plays director and designer will produce further effects like the angling of a ramp that rises to become a wall on which the exhausted Henry exhorts his near-dead troops once more to the breach, and lowers astonishingly to reveal the Katherine of Ludmila Mikaël rising like Venus from the sea after Henry has received the news–shattering, as Mr Howard plays the scene–that Harfleur has surrendered...

I admire Hands's refusal to crucify the play on a stylistic principle, but...I trust that he will drop the stylistic oddity of the present opening, which presents Henry's court as a group of football referees until we are supposed to have eked out Farrah's imperfections with our thoughts...

Meanwhile, the production offers some fine images of Henry's struggle with his destiny (Williams' observation that 'Your Majesty appeared not like himself' becomes an organic growth of the earlier plays) and of troops driven to the limit to enable the king to achieve self-realization...

THE SUNDAY TIMES

HAROLD HOBSON

No words of mine can adequately convey the theatrical, visual, and above all the spiritual splendour of Terry Hands's production of *Henry V*, which opened the RSC Stratford-on-Avon season last Tuesday. *Henry V* is a most difficult play, to which the temper of the time is altogether hostile.

It is full of pageantry, of shining armour and of banners; and today pageantry is something to which we are instinctively unsympathetic. Mr Hands has dealt with our imperfect sympathy by an invention as daring as it is brilliant. He begins the performance by putting his cast into sweaters, football gear and jeans: and then at the precise moment when the audience is utterly weary of this drabness he changes them into costumes that illumine the theatre.

The play's second great contemporary handicap is that it glories in being English. Now to glory in being Welsh, Scottish, or Irish is permissible, and even laudable. But to be proud of being English is generally regarded as bordering on indecency: it makes the delicate blush. A sensitive colleague voices the opinion of the majority of sophisticated playgoers when he describes *Henry V*, with stern disapproval, as 'patriotic tub-thumping.' Mr Hands has done more than conquer this almost universal prejudice: he has used it to make his *Henry V* richer and deeper than I have ever known it to be before.

He has particularly noted that Henry's claim to France was doubtful: and even more he has been affected by that scene on the night before Agincourt when Henry wanders amongst his troops, and in disguise talks to them of their troubles, and is met by the man who tells him what wounds and tribulations war brings to common soldiers.

The magnificence of Mr Hands's production lies simply in this, that his Henry has no need of the instruction. In this incident he used once to be played as a great king and noble warrior comforting his people: but today we see him, Alan Howard plays him, as a man sorely in need of comfort himself, and knowing that he will have to do his best in a terrible situation without it.

For Mr Howard's superb, and I had almost said eclipsing, Henry is not a natural soldier. Whenever war approaches, doubts and distress cloud Mr Howard's face: his Henry is made for other things than war. He fears war: but being in it he acquits himself like a pride of lions, and out of the depths of his anguish he utters some of the most ringing and thrilling calls to valour ever heard in a theatre.

But it is at a great cost that Henry conquers both himself and his opponents; a cost seen most vividly when Harfleur surrenders. Henry faces the audience, and when he hears the news that there will be no further battle the relief of his tension is such that he very nearly breaks down. He is like a man saved at the eleventh hour from hell.

The production is packed with brilliancies: the glitter of the three French nobles in their golden armour just before battle: the scaling of the wall at Harfleur: the kindly gentleness of Emrys James's Chorus: the figure of Oliver Ford-Davies's Herald writing quietly through the night: and the reconciliation of Henry with the soldier who had insulted him. Most brilliant of all perhaps is that *Henry V* is to be followed, not preceded, by *Henry IV*. For if Mr Hands can show us how this man became what we now know that he manifestly was, this will be amongst the greatest seasons in Stratford's history.

DAILY EXPRESS

HERBERT KRETZMER

Threatened by a severe lack of funds and the prospect of fewer American tourists, the Royal Shakespeare Company last night launched its 1975 season with a confident display that encourages the belief that the theatre in Shakespeare's birthplace will yet survive and prosper.

This *Henry V* is stirring stuff, a reminder of national greatness.

And as the Monarch who led a bankrupt and dishevelled army to a famous victory, Alan Howard movingly provides a portrait of English fortitude that will surely be remembered at the end of the year when the 'best actor' awards are judged.

The evening starts deceptively and discouragingly. As members of the audience take their seats the cast is already on stage, standing about wearing track suits, jeans, and sneakers.

As the play proceeds the modern clothing disappears, a huge canopy unfolds and overhangs the action, the actors change into the opulent fashions of the royal courts of England and France–and the shining armour of conflict.

The direction by Terry Hands is impeccable and coherent. At no time is there more than a handful of actors on the stage…'We few, we happy few…' Yet I cannot easily recall a production of this rabble-rousing play that stirred me as much.

Alan Howard brings to the central role a quiet, scholarly intelligence and a willingness to display emotion rare in a British actor.

When the news is brought that against the thousands of French losses at Agincourt 'but five and twenty' English troopers had perished in the battle, Henry's disbelieving exultation is beautiful to witness.

This is a gutsy, reviving production at a time of national adversity. And, boy, do we need it.

NEW STATESMAN

BENEDICT NIGHTINGALE

...Why the rehearsal-room opening? Presumably because Mr Hands fears we'll be ravished and lulled by too much spectacle too soon. He wants us to enter the play in a detached, critical frame of mind, because of the nature of the production he's about to offer us. He is not going to heroise Hal and glamorise conquest, nor does he want to slant things the other way, satirising and condemning a blood-thirsty crusade. He's going to do what few directors nowadays dare, especially with plays as controversial as this: allow us to decide what *we* think, on the lavish and sometimes contradictory evidence Shakespeare himself offers us. And it is an aspiration he fulfills, I would say triumphantly, whether his eye falls on the bland, romantic French court, or on the tattered remnants of the Falstaff gang, or on the bouncing British captains – Trevor Peacock's troglodyte Fluellen, Barrie Rutter's wild MacMorris, and all. The war is neither an inter-European cricket match nor a voracious human abattoir, but a series of encounters that bring the worst out of some and the best out of others: frightening, challenging and above all exhausting. I shan't quickly forget the moment when Farrah's adaptable umbrella-cum-escutcheon is lowered outside-up on to the floor, to become a mass of brown bulges and peaks, halfway between a moonscape and the Flanders mud, upon which a filthy, dazed English army helplessly slumps. *That*, you feel is what it must have been like on the way to Agincourt.

A complex production needs a complex Hal, and gets him in Alan Howard. Mr Howard is all imagination and self-awareness. After he's sentenced the Scroop faction to death, he holds his head and staggers in sudden nausea, as if he could see their chopped necks; and when Harfleur capitulates, he doesn't disguise his relief at missing a similar spectacle. Ghosts haunt his queasy mind, principal among them his own father, usurper of Richard II's throne – witness the hoarse panic of Mr Howard's prayer that this crime should be remembered 'not today, O Lord, O, not today'. As this suggests, he's also a pretty scrupulous sort, always uncomfortable about the responsibilities thrust upon him. 'May I with right and conscience make this claim?' he asks of the invasion of France, his earnest self-doubt quaintly contrasting with the Archbishop's complacent bleating. The production leaves us free to conclude that his military adventure was a moral outrage; but it doesn't give us any reason to suppose that it was lightly or cynically perpetrated by him...

The Daily Telegraph

ERIC SHORTER

If ever a king had need of confidence in his cause it must have been Shakespeare's *Henry V*, revived by Terry Hands for the Royal Shakespeare Company at Stratford-on-Avon last night.

And if ever an actor seemed uncertain of that cause, even of God's support at the crucial moment, it is Alan Howard, whose performance brings to an often over-simplified role a rare, exciting and sincere complexity.

He gives us a sort of queasy and neurotic Christian who is always having profound second thoughts.

And though at times he makes you wonder with his doubts and hesitations whether Hamlet hasn't turned up at Agincourt in error, he goes about his obviously distasteful task with a sufficiently tearful sincerity to draw immediate sympathy.

Mr Howard sees the king as woefully miscast. He himself fits the role – or makes the role fit him – with an impressive integrity – a boyish, pasty-faced youth with a ruminative lower lip and small blue eyes which look for reassurance at once to heaven and into his own heart.

He did not move me greatly, but I felt greatly moved for him, which is perhaps the next best thing...

THE OBSERVER

ROBERT CUSHMAN

Historically kings may be outmoded, but dramatically we miss them.

Drama being an instrument for the apprehension of man, a king interests us partly because exciting things are likely to happen to him, partly because both what he does and what he suffers may affect thousands of others. Most of all, perhaps, the king interests us because he knows all this; there is hardly a moment when he can forget it.

This, of course, is the burden and the magic of Shakespeare's histories, plays which range the country, returning always to a royal base. Its definitive statement is the ceremony speech in *Henry V*, which is now being given searching, imaginative expression by Alan Howard at Stratford. As it should be: this speech follows a debate on the monarch's responsibility to his subjects; it details obsessively the symbols of royalty, describes the concept as a 'proud dream,' but offers no hope that it may be escapable. Henry by now is wedded to his office; nothing else of him is left.

This speech is the summation not only of the play and of Terry Hands's production, but of the whole season...The education of a prince is beyond doubt the subject of *Henry IV*, and it can be demonstrated – though not conclusively proved – that it is that of *Henry V* as well...

Meanwhile Mr Hands's production (which, before I forget, is very good indeed; the best evening I have had at Stratford in ages) presents us with a fascinating, but not altogether convincing, conflict. On the one hand there is Emrys James as the Chorus acclaiming Harry, almost from the outset, as 'the mirror of all Christian kings'; on the other there is Mr

Howard having serious doubts. It takes him until the ceremony speech to become fully king in his own estimation; that he is king in Heaven's he cannot believe until after Agincourt, when he murmurs incredulously 'Oh God, thy arm *was* here.' The early conspiracy against him ('another fall of man') is greeted with agonised shock instead of the customary sanctimonious blandness. In other circumstances, he can put on a good show, a professional imitation of a hero-warrior. The interpretation suits Mr Howard almost too well; he can be rather an effortful actor himself, with a steely but over-obsessive grip on the verse. Like Henry he gets what he wants, which is fine, but you can see him trying, which isn't...

Punch

SHERIDAN MORLEY

Although some tidy scholastic minds are doubtless going to be o'erthrown by the fact that Terry Hands has opened his history cycle at Stratford-on-Avon with *Henry V* (only to return to *Henry IV* later in the month) there can be no doubt that this season's first production represents the Royal Shakespeare Company back at the top of their not inconsiderable form.

On a bare stage, surrounded by actors in tracksuits, an eager if somewhat diminutive Welsh Chorus yearns for a muse of fire and one begins to fear the worst as the Archbishops, nattily attired in White City running plimsolls, start to explain Henry's convoluted claim to France. Evidently the RSC are about to show us, yah boo sucks, that cut-price Shakespeare simply doesn't work and that if the Arts Council won't come up with a better cheque this is how we'll be getting our Bard in the future – and in this context, few Shakespearian scenes so amply illustrate the need for costume as the opening of *Henry V*.

But then, praise be, as Henry decides to go into battle, a gun carriage appears and on it are costumes galore – meanwhile a golden tapestry descends from the grid and we are back in the pageantry business with a simple, stunning stage effect owing more than a little to the moment when, in Olivier's film of this very play, the actors leave the Globe Theatre for real settings.

But the crowning achievement of Mr. Hands' production is to be seen later: having got his Henry (Alan Howard, in the performance of his career) costumed and armed and to France, he then shows us that here is a play about defeat as well as victory; not only the defeat of the French (ably and almost solely personified by Oliver Ford-Davies who appears to have been cast, in one of the production's true economies, as Montjoy, the Governor of Harfleur and most of the French court) but also about the near-defeat of the English who so far from being a band of brothers mindlessly triumphing across the countryside are in fact played as a dissident, near-vanquished troop only eventually shoved into the breach once more by the sheer determination of Henry to prove himself a King able to overcome insuperable odds...

LE FIGARO

JEAN-JACQUES GAUTIER,
de l'Académie française.

La réalisation de la Royal Shakespeare Company, préparée par M. Terry Hands, pour le centenaire du Royal Shakespeare Theatre de Stratford, est, d'un bout à l'autre, une merveille de compréhension et de limpidité. Jamais on ne s'y abandonne à la bassesse d'un effet pour l'effet. Tout: la mise en scène, les déplacements, les attitudes, les gestes et la mimique des comédiens, les éclairages, les éléments de décor et les costumes (de Farrah), tout, dis-je, tout est simple, noble, franc, pur, grandiose et linéaire; mais tout, aussi, est motivé et si intelligent, si lisible, si naturel, que le spectateur a, comme chaque fois qu'il s'agit d'une "chose de beauté", d'une œuvre accomplie, l'impression que tout cela était nécessaire et suffisant, indispensable, voire inévitable et presque immanent. Vous vous dites: "Que pouvait-on faire d'autre?..." Eh! mais autre chose; seulement, c'est le signe de la perfection.

Aux côtés du roi Henri IV d'Angleterre superbement campé, sans nulle grandiloquence, par Emrys James (le Dr Evans des *Joyeuses Commères*) qui, ici, n'est qu'humanité souveraine, j'ai admiré, avec une égale tension et une passion incessantes, du milieu de la matinée à la fin de l'après midi, l'acteur extraordinaire qu'est Alan Howard et qui, à force de finesse, de rare hauteur, d'autorité incisive, et d'inimitable sobriété, prend, sous nos yeus, sa dimension royale.

Il devient le *Henry V* qui, le même soir, va régner sur de turbulentes familles de son pays, débarquer aux rives du nôtre, remporter la victoire d'Azincourt et demander sa main à Catherine, fille de Charles VI et d'Isabeau; "car, dira-t-il, j'aime si fort la France que, refusant d'en perdre un seul village, je la veux tout entière et, dès que la France est à moi, et moi à vous, la France est à vous, et vous êtes moi.."

Le cœur a ses raisons d'Etat que la postérité ne comprend pas toujours.

THE RESPONSE OF THE AUDIENCE

SOME LETTERS TO THE COMPANY.

From Tamsin Rowe, on behalf of her form at the Godolphin School:

We came to see '*Henry V*' on Saturday afternoon. We are studying it for 'O' level, and very much enjoyed the production but it has left us with one or two queries, in particular the following.

We gather from the VIth form who saw *Henry IV Part One*, that that was done 'straight'. How, therefore, can one justify the beginning of *Henry V* in its modern dress, track suits etc, and the rather nonchalent attitude of Henry himself. We wonder very much what was the point of such a beginning and especially what will happen when you do all three together as a trilogy as we believe it should be done. Could you please find the time to elucidate a little. We are very interested and not just because we are doing it for an examination.

From Lyn Morris, Uxbridge, Middlesex.

I have not, up till now, been interested in the Theatre and certainly not in Shakespeare. It was purely by accident that I became involved with visiting the Royal Shakespeare Theatre, but since my first visit some months ago I find that I have never been so enthralled with anything so totally before in my life. It isn't just the plays that have made such an impact, but the actors too, particularly Alan Howard, Brewster Mason and Emrys James. They seem to put themselves wholly into the parts they are playing and put over the characters with such feeling that it's exhausting to watch. I thought it would be so bare without scenery and props, but they really aren't necessary. Through *Henry V* and *Henry IV Part Two* (the only two I've seen so far) I was so involved with what was going on that a Mickey Mouse Cartoon could have been going on in the background and I would never have noticed.

From Daphne Armer, Knowle (to Terry Hands)

A friend and I came to see your *Henry V* the other night, and like the critic in *The Times*, we are puzzled by those

259

strange figures limbering up at the beginning of the play. We would be most grateful if you could enlighten us (and incidentally our friends who are also going to see it) - are they footballers, and if so, why?

We just couldn't see the connection, and neither did we like the tennis balls scene played in mufti; I know the play backwards, but for others who aren't so familiar with it, the whole scene must have presented a puzzle, especially with all those titles flying around.

Otherwise, we thought the production splendid - esp. the costumes and the effects; the tapes of the battle scene came over terrifyingly well, though with all those extra lights we felt sorry for the players - I counted 80 that I could see, and I expect there were more.

So if you could spare a few minutes from your hectic life, I should be glad to know what the footballers are supposed to represent. Bless you for resisting the temptation to 'tart up' Shakespeare; the play really came alive–especially with a real French princess. We're having bets on what the 'jelly mould' up in the flies will represent in *Henry IV*!

From Professor Guy Butler, Rhodes University, Grahamstown, S.A. (to Terry Hands)

This is the first time in my 25 years as an academic, whose main interest is Shakespeare, that I have written to congratulate a producer on one of his plays. I refer to your *Henry V*, which I saw in Stratford last Monday. Not that I have seen *no* other productions that moved my admiration: but I have frequently been more irritated then delighted by the brilliance and ingenuity etc of the producer, who is usually, it seems to me, far more concerned with using the text as a trapeze on which to play his own fantastic tricks, than as a sacred and mysterious thing which he must use all his talents and resources to lift off the page into life.

I had my moments of apprehension during the opening, but the polo-jersey bridging device pays off. It does so, I think, because it presents no enticements to the eye, and obliges the audience first to give its total attention to the language–which, praise God, was spoken as *verse*, not broken

into the grunts and groans of 'realistic' theatre. Somewhere
Yeats cries:

> *But actors lacking music*
> *Do most enrage my spleen -*
> *They think it is more human*
> *To shuffle, grunt and groan*
> *Not knowing what unearthly stuff*
> *Rounds a mighty scene.*

You persuaded yourself, and your actors etc, that the scene
was mighty, and the 'unearthly stuff' came across and bowled
me over. Surprises and discoveries everywhere. I had the usual
anti-jingo, anti-heroic hang-ups, but I came away convinced
that I had not read the work with the kind of attention that
it deserves. I have re-read it since, with far deeper insight.
It so happens that I am taking my honours class for
Elizabethan drama, and it struck me, dealing with *Tamburlaine*
yesterday p.m., that *Henry V* is Shakespeare's reply—*his*
version of the great warrior monarch....

From Joanne Loftus, Northwich, Cheshire. '*a faithful and eternal*
fan', *to Alan Howard*)

When I was staying in Stratford-upon-Avon for the weekend
I saw your performance. You're the most fantastic actor I
have ever seen and gorgeous looking with it. Although I'm
only 14 yrs old, I do have heroes, and I've moved David
Essex down to second place, just to put you at the top.

From Natalie Ward, Wellesbourne, Warwickshire (to Alan
Howard).

In most other productions of the *Henry IV/V* plays I have
seen the character of Hal is not allowed to develop in any
great depth. There almost seems to be the feeling that to be
such a great man and leader Hal must be cold and impersonal,
without any soul. This, I feel, is where you succeed with Hal.
He suffers; Hal is as vulnerable as we all are. As a prince
he enjoys the company of Falstaff and his followers, even
though he considers it an apprenticeship for king-ship; the
same man as king must throw off these cronies and allow
Bardolph to be executed. That Henry does this doesn't mean

that he can remain apart from his actions; at times they tear his soul apart and the fact that you allow Henry to be human brings the play to the greater emotional depths that most other productions have failed to reach for me. 'Upon the King! Let us, our lives, our souls,/ Our debts, our careful wives, Our Children and our sins, lay on the King,' says Henry before the battle of Agincourt and one is made aware of the weight of responsibility that Hal is made to bear from the moment he takes the crown believing his father dead. Your interpretation of Henry's character doesn't make him a 'super-human Batman', he is an integral part of the whole, and he lives, not simply exists......

From Mr. T. H. Foster, a company Director, (to Terry Hands)

I have six tickets for the Gala Performance of *Henry V* on 27th June. I was looking forward to attending, but was horrified to learn from a friend that the performance of *Henry V* is to be given with the actors dressed in boiler suits or similar garb. I cannot believe this is true for such a performance, especially with Royalty present, so perhaps you will advise me what the true situation is please, and I shall then know whether to take up my tickets or not.

I hope you will not be offended by my attitude as everyone is entitled to their views in this matter, but I would not enjoy the performance unless the costumes were authentic to the period and in keeping.

Shoreditch School
Falkirk Street
London N.1
30th September 1975

Dear Mr Howard

If you remember that while
you were showing us around the back stage one
of the school party asked if the cannon was
light and you said I don't think so and one
said but only three men pulled it with you on top
Well the one who said that is me Tony Lowen
and firstly I would like to say that I though
I have never been to a theatre before enjoyed it
better that watching any tv program mostly for
the actors being live and there in front of
them (the audience), also when we done
a project of Shakespeare last term I got
a prize (a book of Shakespeares collected plays) and
on getting home I looked up some parts of the
play and looking at the words on the paper I
realised what a very good actor you were and how
talented you have to be before you can get a part
like yours. If I was talking to you I know I would
ask you are you interested in Shakespeare but
Seeing that I am not talking to you you can't
answer me but if I ever see another play
of Willy Shakes I hope you are in it (try
macbeth for instance).

I was talking mrs Smith
a few days ago and she said that you as well
as playing in a comedy a few times she saw you
on Churchills people which unfortunately I
missed. but I am sure you played a good part few
when I saw you playing henry V I dubbed you
actor of the year.

Now I must end this letter for time is
running short on this leson so I must say how
gratfull we are on you showing us around the
back stage (probably giving us some of your
time) and I wish you all the luck in the
future for future sucess (hamlet maybe),

your sincerly

AJ lonen